EXPERIENCES WITH *Living Things*

EXPERIENCES WITH

Living Things

AN INTRODUCTION TO ECOLOGY

FOR FIVE- TO EIGHT-YEAR-OLDS

by KATHERINE WENSBERG

WITH DRAWINGS BY PAT KENT

Unitarian Universalist Association, Boston

IN APPRECIATION

THE AUTHOR is certain this book would not have been written had it not been for the encouragement and the help of Dr. Dorothy Spoerl, who inspired its structural plan, wrote the portion of each chapter headed "Other Possible Experiences," and compiled the lists of recommended books with their helpful thumbnail descriptions. Her foreword is an essential part of the book, and her ideas have influenced every page.

Thanks are due to many for assistance of various kinds, all greatly appreciated:

To Dr. Martin Kushner, Seattle, Washington, for well-timed encouragement and the loan of reference material.

To Mrs. Florence Whitman, Turner, Maine, who first used the stories with children and suggested that a wealth of experience precede the storytelling.

To Mrs. Margaret Gooding of Tempe, Arizona, who made suggestions for adaptation to the desert environment.

To Miss E. Marie Boyle, science author and teacher, Havertown, Pennsylvania, who looked for scientific inaccuracies in the book and saved us from passing on misinformation.

To Mrs. Ruby Aoyama, Bellevue, Washington; Mrs. Eileen Day, Wellesley Hills, Massachusetts; and Mrs. Barbara Rosen,

Mercer Island, Washington, who tried the experiences and stories with groups of children during the writing.

To the children, staff, and director of *The Little School* of Seattle, Washington, where the author, while teaching, learned more about young children and was greatly helped while planning this book.

K. W.

Seattle, Washington

CONTENTS

FOREWORD

A LITTLE TIME spent in watching children of kindergarten and
early elementary age will soon reveal their tremendous curiosity
about and interest in living things. Sometimes from our adult
point of view this interest seems out of proportion to the plant,
insect, bird, or creature observed. For we have virtually forgot-
ten the first time we watched the ant crawling over a leaf of grass
while holding an oversize crumb; or the day we too stood en-
tranced while a robin carried string after string, bit after bit of
mud to the nest we could not quite see; or the fascination of
watching grasshopper, cricket, and bee.

How can we start with this natural curiosity of the child
and move on to deepen it? How can we help him find his own
meanings, and yet open up to him meanings beyond his immediate experience? How can we add facts which enlarge his view and
not become didactic and encyclopedic? How can we help open
up for him the truly spiritual concept of the interrelationships
and the interdependence of all living things? In *Experiences
with Living Things: An Introduction to Ecology for Five- to
Eight-Year-Olds,* Katherine Wensberg has done these things and
more.

She has been able to do them because she herself has these

spiritual concepts, as evidenced by these words from a talk she gave on nursery school science,

> I consider basic to the development of a mature religion an understanding gained early and thus never lost of the interdependence of all living things. This understanding accepts all life as linked not only to everything else that lives but to the elements of the physical world. It is the understanding that led to St. Francis of Assisi's "Hymn of Creation" in which he refers to "our brother, the sun" and "our sister, the moon," "our brother, fire" and "our sister, water" and "our mother, earth." St. Francis was so at home with the universe he knew, that all parts of it seemed related to him, as of course they are now under-stood to be related to all of us, since we are made of that related, very active matter, sometimes called "the stuff of the universe."
>
> Giving children experiences to learn from, rather than information alone, teaches them to discover, test, ask about, evaluate, and not accept blindly what they are told. The things we really *know* and therefore live by we learn this way.

THE CONCEPT OF ECOLOGY

Whenever man has opened a new area of scientific explora-tion, he has had to find a name for it. *Ecology* came into our lan-guage during the twentieth century. It is a Greek word meaning "study of the home," used scientifically to identify the study of plants and animals in relation to their environment. This study includes the relationship of man to his environment of plant and animal life, and to the earth, air, sun, and water upon which all living things depend.

Because children are eager to learn about the natural world around them, there can be an early introduction to ecology. Children recognize their immediate outdoor surroundings as part of their home. They want to find out all they can about what lives there. A study of ecology by young children will prove most successful if it comes as a result of their own exploration. Guiding such an adventure can be a matter of providing resources for the answering of questions and giving the kind of adult leadership, stimulation, and direction which keeps the activity of a group of young children exciting and rewarding.

This book is planned as a guide for the leader who undertakes backyard exploration with boys and girls of kindergarten and early primary age. Small groups (never more than twelve) will have the best time and learn the most. The experiences described in this guide are rich and varied and should always precede any storytelling. Experience first, with story and discussion afterwards, is the most effective framework for teaching children of these ages. A child cannot form a theory about the interdependence of living things while he is still full of questions about a specific grasshopper! But after he has had a chance to satisfy his active curiosity (and this may require several class sessions), he can then review his own experience as he listens to a story about the experiences of others.

The underlying reason for teaching ecology to the children of early elementary age is our conviction that children who grow up with some understanding of the intricate interweaving of the web of life will always feel more a part of the universe. They will always be more intelligently aware of what goes on in the natural world about them, no matter where they are at every moment of the day or night. They may live in a world where machines have increasing attention, but they will know the value of living things and will continue to seek answers to their continuing questions about life in its myriad forms.

THE PLAN OF THIS BOOK

There are several special features in the plan of this book which should be kept carefully in mind if the full value of the experience with living things is to be realized.

First, the chapters are presented in terms of a rich variety of experiences the teacher can make available to the children. Not every experience will be used with each topic, but the actual working with materials and creatures should continue so long as the interest of the children lasts. It is the *experience* which is most important of all; give the children ample time to savor this.

Second, when the teacher feels that the children have gained all that they are going to gain, at this time, from the firsthand experience, then is the time to turn to the story which is given at the end of each experience. These stories are emphatically NOT introductions to the experience, but rather summaries of it. They contain a good many facts and explanations; used as an introduction they would be didactic and far too encyclopedic. But used *after* the children have done the things described, they become a recapitulation of the child's own experience, and the eagerness with which children listen to this kind of review makes possible the addition of extra facts and knowledge. Many of these facts and most of the interpretations will already have been talked about with the children in the process of helping them find answers to their questions. The stories are, in other words, a review of the experience in capsule form.

Third, there are bibliographic references for each of the experiences which are important to them. Even kindergarten children who cannot yet read will pore over the pictures in the books that are recommended, and the leader will perhaps read them *portions* of the book that help to answer questions raised. This serves the dual purpose of finding answers to the questions without the leader's always "knowing the answer," and of introducing children to the concept of books as rich resources to be used in daily living. If the books are not brought into the classroom the depth of the experience will be lost.

Fourth, these experiences are not planned to cover any specific length of time. Some of them may be savored by the children over a period of three to five weeks, others might involve less time, and an occasional experience may cover an even greater time. Sometimes a creature not included among the living things in this volume will capture the interest of the group, in which case the teacher will want to devise a wide variety of experiences with this living thing and trace its existence as a part of the web of life, which does, indeed, include *all* living things.

Fifth, to help weave together all the experiences and deepen the appreciation of the children for the delicate balance of life in which all living things depend on other living things, a song which the children will continue is woven into some of the stories. This the teacher will want to introduce and watch for the children to accept spontaneously as a part of their own experience, so that hopefully they will begin to add their own lines to this "House That Jack Built" kind of song, which will dramatically review for them the intricate interrelationships described.

Experience is the best of all teachers, and the leader who will follow the plan of the book will discover that many meanings that adults might not give to these experiences will emerge from the children's own eager interest. Allow much time for experience and discussion, for pictures and for books, and for dramatics and art and dancing. Recall constantly that words are the child's weakest vehicle of communication, and only when the group is ready for it can the summary story at the end of the experience be used. It should be a happy experience throughout for teacher and children alike.

THE CLASSROOM SETTING

The classroom should be equipped with shelves on which treasured objects may be saved; and the teacher should be ready to provide temporary cages for living things the children may want to examine more closely than they can in the out-of-doors. (These living things should be released at the end of the class session, by the child, and returned to their natural environment. This is a basic conservation concept that no child can learn too early.) There are a few basic books that the leader will want for a reference shelf, for these will give help at many points along the way:

A set of the Zim nature guides, put out by the Golden Press, and easily available everywhere, will be valuable for their many pictures, and for the help they give in identification.

In addition these are books which have been found particularly useful in all kinds of science teaching with elementary aged children:

Brown, Vinson. *How To Make a Home Nature Museum.* Little.
Brown, Vinson, *How To Make a Miniature Zoo.* Little.

Hillcourt, William. *Field Book of Nature Activities*. Putnam.

Saunders, John R. *Golden Book of Nature Crafts*. Golden Press.

Blough, G. O., and Huggett, Albert J. *Elementary-School Science and How to Teach It*. Dryden Press (Holt, Rinehart & Winston).

Blough, G. O., and Campbell, Marjorie H. *Making and Using Classroom Science Materials in the Elementary School*. Dryden Press (Holt, Rinehart & Winston).

Hone, E. B., Joseph A., Victor E. *A Sourcebook for Elementary Science*. Harcourt.

American Association for the Advancement of Science and the National Science Foundation. *A Selected List of Paper-bound Science Books: An Inexpensive Science Library*. American Association for the Advancement of Science, 1515 Massachusetts Ave., N.W., Washington, D.C. 20005 (25 cents)

Aside from these books for the teacher's general use and the books listed with each experience, there are a few basic science materials which should be in the room from the beginning. These are materials useful throughout the school, and quite essential for the study of any living things.

10x magnifiers, and a variety of magnifying glasses of less power.

For the younger children (although it will be eagerly used by the older ones as well) there is a "Giant Magnifier on Stand," of 5x magnification, which is a real addition to classroom equipment. Catalog number KS374, this is available for $9.95 plus postage (3 lbs. 2 oz.) from Creative Playthings, Inc., Princeton, New Jersey 08540.

Each leader will want to build up certain resources of his own for the classroom as well:

a. Poetry books which contain poems about living things. Songbooks covering the same materials.

b. Records of bird songs, or insect sounds, which can be played when the occasion arises.

c. A file of carefully mounted pictures, which can be used to enrich the environment as a new experience is introduced, to be used as resource materials, and to be referred to as experiences are reviewed.

d. As each new experience is introduced a browsing table containing the books in the bibliography at the end of each chapter should be available. (Any of these which are owned by the school should be in the room all the time, but placed on the table for each experience.) Most of these books can be borrowed from public libraries for the time of the study, some the school will surely want to purchase so as to begin an adequate basic library, and many will be found in the children's homes if a letter of inquiry is sent out listing the books which are wanted. Parents may be quite willing to purchase one or two books as their contribution to their child's experience.

The richer the environment the richer will be the children's experience. Do not expect that every book, every picture, every object will be used and examined by every child, but let there be enough available so that the constant *invitation to explore* is open.

THE SHARING OF EXPERIENCE

The teacher will want to keep constantly in mind that this group of experiences is not intended for the "teaching of science," but rather for sharing with children many experiences with living things, and helping them to investigate each of these on their own, with the hope of their developing deep appreciations about interrelatedness and interdependence. The teacher will *share* these experiences with the children, looking with them, talking with them, wondering with them, and helping them to use the resources of both the natural environment and the classroom.

Children's concepts develop slowly; repetition of experiences, time for wondering and for evolving tentative answers, richness of pictures and books, all these contribute their share to the concept.

Experience is to be the teacher, not the class leader. Experience in exploring, experience in discussing, experiences with books, music, poetry, and the expressive experiences of art, the dance, and the creation of poetry and song. All of these are the media of teaching, shared equally by the children and the leader.

And so we send *Experiences with Living Things* out to the children that they may learn through their own doing, and to the leaders so that they may teach through the sharing of experience. And the hope is that this will be an experience long to be remembered by all who embark upon it.

DOROTHY T. SPOERL, Editor

Berkeley, California

INTRODUCTORY EXPERIENCE

IN PREPARING for the first meeting of children and leader, the adult must try to imagine how the children will be feeling. They will be curious about each other, for some or all of the boys and girls will be strangers to one another. They will be curious about their leader. And the children will be curious about what they are going to do, although their parents should have been informed ahead of time about the nature of the year's activities.

If each child (and the adult as well) gives his name, an introduction has been made, but something more self-revealing than a name is needed. Has the child any pets? What does he enjoy as a special hobby? Where does he go to school? The giving of such clues to personality makes everyone feel better acquainted.

The leader will tell in general terms what kind of experiences are to come, and the room itself will help to reveal that these children are to be a group of explorers, beginning-scientists in a way, learning to use eyes, ears, hands, and brains in discovering things. They will also use magnifying glasses, and possibly microscopes, as well as other tools. A table will contain such equipment, including a sample of various screened and covered containers, digging tools, measuring tapes, and other paraphernalia that may come into use later. There should be pictures

1

on display of people digging, dipping specimens out of water, climbing over rocks, gathering shells, observing live creatures, and having the kinds of experiences the children are to have. Art materials and examples of child art showing animals or plants or people (anything alive) should decorate the room. Objects new to the children add interest to the first impression. It will be apparent to everyone that much of the time ahead is to be spent out of doors.

Obviously, if the experiences to come are to be genuine explorations and discoveries, the exact subject matter will not be mentioned. Nor will there be any reference to the word "ecology" or to the interdependence of living things.

Plans must be made for the next meeting at this first one, so the leader must really prepare for both in advance. The next one is to be the first outdoor experience, and it is recommended that it be the experience with sand. None of the others described in these pages need follow in the order given here, but the stories used throughout the year to summarize each experience are about a family, and this family will be met in the story "Where the Sand Comes From." Therefore it is good to start with this experience. All children and most adults enjoy handling wet sand and working or playing with it. The places where it is found are exciting to visit. In such an informal, enjoyable experience, a good start can be made.

At the first meeting the group can begin to plan a work party, the nature of which the leader can describe to them. In the planning (and later, the enjoyment) of a work party each child will gain confidence in the others, in the teacher, and in his own ability to do and be what is expected of him. After this reassuring confidence begins to warm the atmosphere, the class will feel and act like a group, and everyone in it can look forward with eagerness to what lies ahead.

The date will be set for a work party, to be held either between regular meetings or at the time of the next one. Some simple division of duties can be worked out for food, for cleanup, telephoning, and helping in other ways. Clothing will be discussed, for playclothes or workclothes will be required according to the nature of the project to be carried out.

Since the first story is about sand the ideal place for the work party would be an ocean, or lake, beach where each child would make a collection of rocks of graduated sizes, the largest being one that fits the palm of his hand. If there is no beach, a mountain stream or a swift river with shores safe for picnickers will be fine, or desert sand, or whatever natural sand is to be found in the area. Should none of these be near enough, there are alternatives appropriate to the sand theme. For instance, at the regular meeting place a sandbox can be built and filled with sand for the use of this group and other children. In this case the work party would be at "home base."

If the leader knows someone with a rock tumbler and a rock collection, the work party could include a visit to watch the action of the tumbler, giving the children a chance to learn the secret beauty that lies within rough unpolished stone.

Wherever the work party is held, after the fun, the work, the food, and some of the suggested activities, there can be a quieter time when the introductory story is read, "Where the Sand Came From." Better yet, the leader can tell the story in his own words. More of the activities can follow the story in this instance, although in later studies most of the activities should be worked through until the children have thoroughly explored the subject before the summarizing story is told.

1. A single grain of sand can be examined under a 10x magnifier.

2. Pieces of sandstone can be rubbed together or pounded to make sand. (Don't try to do this with granite or marble!)

3. A miniature seaside can be made. If an indoor party is necessary, a sandtable can be used in place of the sandbox for this. Water is poured into a part of the box (or if the box is not waterproof a piece of mirror can be substituted.) Then small shells are placed along the water's edge, toy boats and bathers scattered along the beach. Such materials as paper, clay, pipe cleaners, odd-shaped scraps of wood, thumbtacks, glue, and either real shells or shell macaroni can be used. If the children are at a real beach they can make a miniature one out of materials at hand.

4. An alternative to the miniature beach is a sand mountain with a stream bed running down its side, using twigs, small rocks, and real water trickling down from a hose buried under cotton snow on the peak. A plastic sheet can be spread under an indoor sand table.

> (*If the creations described in 3 or 4 are built they should be photographed when completed so the children can have a permanent record of this part of the experience.*)

5. Rocks of different sizes can be arranged in a graduated row down to pebbles and a single grain of sand.

6. If there is a gentle slope, the children can act out in a game or dance one part of the story. Holding hands to make a long line, they can "swish up the sloping sandy beach in one great curling wave, then roll, roll, roll right back again." Thus they are first the wave, carrying the stone up the beach, and then the stone itself, rolling back down to the sea, only to go up again and again as described in the story. If this can be accompanied by music or a chant it will be more enjoyable.

Whatever is undertaken, it should become the children's own project and can be fun rather than a demonstration. As Emma Sheehy says in *Children Discover Music and Dance*, "One has to consider thoughtfully whether it is *the teacher who is creating by using children* or whether she is the kind of person who really releases children to *create in their own ways.*"

In preparation for this experience with sand, then, the leader must have selected the place for the work party before the first meeting when it will be discussed and duties assigned. Transportation will have to be arranged in advance if the site is distant, and a parent or other adult invited to accompany the children. Lists must be made of everything needed, time allotted for each part of the project, and a little schedule made out for the leader's own use.

The unexpected will happen, nice things not anticipated, minor mishaps, oversights, and pleasant surprises. As always the leader will need to remember that subject matter is never as important as personalities and emotional needs. What is desired is a first experience that makes a second one something to be anticipated. It is inevitable that in the course of events the children will have learned something about sand and its origin . . . and through study of this nonliving thing, they will soon discover the creature which is to give them their first group experience with a most interesting live one.

OTHER POSSIBLE EXPERIENCES WITH SAND

Some groups will want to continue the experience with sand for a longer period of time. Others may not find the suggested activities quite suitable for their particular circumstances. These further suggestions are for the examination of sand from as many points of view as possible, including of course its sound and texture as well as its point of origin. It is never expected that any single group will use all of the experiences which are listed as "possible."

1. Watching sand in an egg timer, turning it and watching again. Noting that it goes at just one speed, that it is steady. The teacher may comment that this is a way of keeping time for short periods, and once was used as a basis for clock making. Time in general is not of particular interest to the younger children in this age range.

2. Making patterns with rocks, not a permanent mosaic, but laying designs out on sand, or on colored paper, for the sheer fun of feeling the texture of the rocks, and admiring their color and form, as well as for the joy of making designs.

3. Color sand so that the children can "paint with sand." Do not call this "sand painting," which confuses it with the Indian ritual, but "painting with sand," which becomes a new medium for making of design and one that is fascinating to children. Sand is colored by the addition of dry powder paint.

4. The older children could also do sand casting, where a design is drawn deeply or pressed into wet sand, or where such things as shells, pine cones, stones, are pressed in and then removed. Plaster of paris is then poured over this and allowed to

set, which gives a design in relief. This is an activity which needs to be carefully supervised, and the younger children will need help. Care should be taken that none of the children taste or eat the plaster of paris (and they do taste so many things). Ideally sand casting would be done out of doors, but it is possible in a sandbox, or in large cartons of sand used for this purpose only.

5. Coloring on sandpaper (again do not confuse this with sand painting, which it is not), gives the child a chance to see the effect of texture on his crayons, and often will help remove the stereotypes developed by the too frequent use of crayons in authoritarian situations.

6. Sand blocks can be made by pasting sandpaper onto any kind of wooden block, and rubbing these together to make an interesting rhythm sound. (The sound will differ according to the fine or coarse nature of the sandpaper used.) Some of the children can do this while others make "box rattles" (boxes filled with pebbles) and experiment with rhythm. Then the children may want to see how they could put these two kinds of sound together to express some of the thoughts they have had during their work or during the story. This is not the old-fashioned kind of "rhythm band" where the children are directed to use instruments with music, but a creative experimentation with sound and rhythm. It doesn't even have to be called music, though it is of course the base from which some music develops.

7. The use of water from a hose can help the children discover how strong a force is needed to carry a rock down an incline, and would thus dramatize for the children the surging strength of a mountain stream in the spring.

BOOKS FOR THE CHILDREN'S USE

The books listed below can be used by the teacher as supplementary material, as resource material for hunting clues to answers, as a place for finding pictures that will answer questions, and for general browsing by the children. A book-rich environment is one of the most valuable forms of stimulation for a child.

Since the experience with sand is only introductory to the study of living things only a few sand books are mentioned; most of those in this particular list are general books covering a wide variety of living things. These should be available throughout all of the experiences, and the more the children browse through them the more likely it is that they will begin to meet these now-familiar creatures in their own environment.

Children's Books About Sand

Clark, Ann Nolan. *Tia Maria's Garden*. Viking.
The desert with its sand, and yet its many living things. A lovely book.

Myrus, Don. *Story in the Sand*. Macmillan.
Photographs which encourage artistic expression with natural materials, and stimulate awareness of textures and shapes.

Children's Books About Nature
General

Conklin, Gladys. *We Like Bugs*. Holiday House.
Great variety, just introduces each briefly, but wonderful browsing table material which may lead to search for "new friends."

Cooper, Elizabeth. *Science in Your Own Backyard*. Harcourt.
Simple and fascinating experiments with nature close at hand, particularly for the older children.

Gibson, Gertrude H. *About Insects That Help Plants*. Melmont.
Ants, grubs, bees, butterflies — a wide variety of insects which interrelate with plants.

Green, Mary McB. *Everybody Eats*. William R. Scott.
Helps a child see the needs of all living things.

Huntington, Harriet. *Let's Go Outdoors*. Doubleday.
Photographs and a brief text, but an excellent introduction to the world of nature.

Stevens, Carla. *Catch a Cricket*. William R. Scott.
How to catch a worm, firefly, cricket, grasshopper, and so forth. Suggestions as to where to find, how to keep, and when to release. Valuable book, with excellent photographs.

Adult Books About Insects

    Lanham, Uri. *The Insects.* Columbia University Press.
    Significant and thought-provoking information about
    insects in general.

SONGS AND POEMS TO USE

All the songs and poems are from three books of the Beacon Press:

    We Sing of Life (edited by Vincent Silliman).
    Martin and Judy Songs (compiled by Edith Lovell Thomas).
    Poems To Grow On (compiled by Jean McKee Thompson).

"Play on the Seashore": Number 66 in *We Sing of Life*
"Sandpile Town": page 61 in *Poems To Grow On.*

STORY TO SUMMARIZE THE EXPERIENCE

WHERE THE SAND CAME FROM

ONCE a great rock broke away from the side of a mountain and
rolled down, down, down. As it rolled it struck other pieces of
rock on the mountain's side and this made it break into hun-
dreds of smaller pieces.

One of the smaller pieces splashed into a stream of water.
The stream was very full that morning because snow was melting on top of the mountain and every tiny trickle of snow water
ran down until it found a stream to join. Water can move a
heavy object like a small rock if the water is flowing fast enough,
so the piece of rock began to travel.

The stream carrying the piece of rock grew fuller and wider.
It rushed and tumbled down the steep slopes with a roar. Other
streams flowed into it and it became a river.

As the river hurried along, on and on, over stones and sand,
the piece of rock went with it down the mountainside, turning
in the water. Its rough sharp edges were scraped away by the
rough, hard parts of the ground it struck under the water.

Sometimes the rock stayed in one place for a long time, held
there by a fallen tree or a larger rock in the river bed. But it always got free when the river water pushed hard enough to move

whatever was holding it. Then the small rock could begin to travel again.

By this time the rough edges were all gone. The rock was smooth and round. It had become a stone that would fit into your hand like a ball.

As many rivers do, this one flowed into an ocean; so one day the stone came to rest on a sandy beach.

Great oceans don't rush downhill like a mountain stream, or flow along with the speed of a river, but they are never quiet. The waves of the ocean carried the small white stone up on the beach and left it there. But soon a stronger wave came in and started it rolling back down again.

This kept happening all the time. Swish up the sloping sandy beach in one great curling wave, then roll, roll, roll right back again. Every time it happened the little round stone had some of itself scraped away on the sand.

Years and years and years went by.

Finally the stone was no larger than a pebble.

Finally it was a very tiny pebble indeed.

Finally it was one small grain of sand on the great ocean beach.

One day a tall boy named Jim came to the beach. He dug some of the clean white sand with a shovel and put it into a cloth bag. He placed the heavy bag in the trunk of a car. He drove to the city nearby and there, in his own backyard, he poured the sand into a sandbox.

Jim didn't tell his two younger brothers and his little sister what he had done. He just called to them to come and see a surprise.

"Hey, Alan!" he called. "Ann and Tom! Come and see what's out here."

The three younger children had been wanting some new sand for a long time and they were so glad to see the full sand-box that they whooped with joy and ran to play in it.

They didn't know they were playing with something that had once been a rock on a mountain side. They didn't know that hot sun melting snow on top of a mountain had made a stream that carried the rock down to the ocean. They didn't know the waves had helped to make their sand.

But right away the children began to fill cans with sand and to pile it up into mountains. They poured water into the sandbox and made little rivers and lakes and oceans.

The sandbox was under a tree on the lawn. It was soon the busiest place in the backyard, and from it, during the weeks to come, the children discovered things they didn't know about what was living all around them.

INTRODUCTION TO THE EXPERIENCE TO FOLLOW

Before parting, unless another class session is to be devoted to the subject of sand, the leader can build up anticipation of the next experience. It will not be necessary to mention what is to be the subject of exploration. It can be done in some such way as this:

If the leader has selected earthworms as the next theme, the children can be asked to pick up a handful of soil, thinking of all the other names for it: dirt, earth, ground, etc.

"Do we know how soil is made?"

"Is it made the same way as sand?"

"Look around you. Where did it all come from?"

"Is it still being made?"

"Can we see it happen?"

"Could we even make some soil? That plants would grow in?"

The leader gives no answers, but if the idea appeals to the children proper digging clothes must be described. Parents can well be told in notes what clothing is required, including rain clothes in case of rain. Such advance preparation a full week ahead of time will save many phone calls and misunderstandings. It also allows the boys and girls to look forward to an adventure that involves digging, something everyone enjoys. *Earthworms have not been mentioned. But they will be discovered.*

Earthworms

DEVELOPING THE EXPERIENCE

ALTHOUGH THE CLASS will come to this meeting looking forward to digging in search of different kinds of soil (as indeed they will do), the teacher who has read the story at the end of this experience knows that the hope is to discover an earthworm which will lead to the study of the first living creature in the children's exploration of their environment.

This little burrowing animal is full of surprises and interest as a subject for study. Darwin, after devoting his genius to a detailed study of earthworms, said of them, ". . . it may be doubted if there are any other animals which have played such an important part in the history of the world as these lowly organized creatures."

Everyone would know more about earthworms if they were not under ground for safety's sake almost all of their lives. The subterranean habits of these helpless animals have made it possible for them to be successful in establishing themselves everywhere. Even at night when earthworms are active, they seldom leave the burrows in which they live, but either extend their anterior end out of the ground to find parts of plants on which to feed, or their posterior end to deposit small piles of coiled dirt called "castings" which are frequently seen on the surface in the morning. Castings are most plentiful when leaves are not abun-

11

dant and the earthworm must find food in the soil. He does this by swallowing the soil and digesting organic materials in it (decayed plant material, seeds, eggs, or larvae and the bodies of small insects, for example). What is not retained, passes out of the anus to make castings.

In hot weather earthworms avoid drying by staying far below the surface. In cold weather they close off their burrows from the upper air and go to a widened chamber at the bottom of the burrow where several worms may be all rolled up together for the winter. In rainy weather worms may come to the surface of the ground because of a lack of oxygen. Although they can live for some time in ordinary water as subaquatic animals do, the water that filters down through the earth loses its oxygen and fills the burrows so the worms are unable to breathe.

Ralph Buchsbaum, zoologist-author of *Animals Without Backbones,* says of earthworms, "The quantity of earth brought up from below and deposited on the surface has been estimated to be as high as eighteen tons per acre per year, or, if spread out uniformly, about two inches in ten years. Seeds are covered and so enabled to germinate, and stones and other objects on the surface become buried. In this way ancient buildings have been covered and so preserved, much to the advantage of archaeologists."

In the digesting of food from the soil there is an efficient kind of "cultivation" because the earthworm has a gizzard and it grinds up what the worm ingests. Since this includes both soil and the remains of uneaten bits of leaves previously pulled down into the ground, these become mixed in the process of grinding. Earthworm castings thus enrich the soil for the production of plant growth.

All that a leader can learn about earthworms will benefit the children because it will add adult enthusiasm to that of the group. Children always know what they are doing is important if they see that the adult sharing their experiences is obviously as interested as they are. A warning is necessary, however, about the way the leader's knowledge is to be used. Much detailed information of great interest to an adult should be left for future discovery by the children when they are older. *Interest* is what we wish to arouse now, so boys and girls will continue to seek out the answers to questions, many of which they will not ask at this age.

The leader's knowledge is a resource for them to probe, as are the books in the classroom, the pictures, and the visual aids of other kinds provided from time to time. The books recommended for such a library are selected because they are the best available on the subject *written for children.* If a teacher volunteers too much information which has not been requested by anyone in the class, general interest may be dulled rather than stimulated. However, the leader can ask questions or wonder aloud in order to arouse interest.

"If all the earthworms in every yard," the leader might ask, "are bringing soil from below up to the top of the ground, I wonder how much of it they move in a whole year?" There need be no answer, but the children's imaginations may be stirred by the wondering.

Forgetting the details about earthworms for the moment, let's now return to considering the coming meeting of the group. What preparation is needed?

Since there is to be digging, each child will need a digging tool: a large spoon, a trowel, or a small spade. If they are to explore the soil, the place for it must be decided. The leader will need to make arrangements in advance, of course, if someone's yard or a nearby park is to be used. Small heavy glass or plastic bottles are recommended for keeping specimens of differing kinds of soil: topsoil from under bushes or trees containing a dark, spongy, absorbent material called *humus,* which is formed by dead plant and animal material; clay, often found close to a building's foundations where it was brought up to the surface during the excavation of the basement; sandy earth from around the sandbox if nowhere else. These specimens can be examined later under magnification if the children wish.

During the digging the nature of the soil reveals itself, and if it is possible to pour water into each variety of soil after it is uncovered, the children can see what happens to rain when it reaches that kind of earth. When the soil is back in the classroom put a half tumblerful of each kind on the shelf and pour a quarter of a cup of water into each tumbler. Then the children can observe how the water goes down into the soil, and the rate at which this happens.

Hopefully, during the digging the children will discover the first earthworm. In expectation of this the leader should have glass jars ready and a hammer and nail so each child preparing a jar full of soil and earthworms (more will be found) can make holes in the lid before covering the jar. (In case no earthworm is found the teacher needs an emergency supply on hand, for this experience introduces the concept of living things in the environment. She will of course have tried out the digging place ahead of time to be reasonably sure it is a good spot for earthworm discovery. The children may spontaneously start asking why they are not finding any.) After earthworms have been put in glass jars for observation a sheet of black paper should be wrapped around the jar when no one is watching the activity inside, thus keeping the earthworms more comfortable.

If the children find any other creatures in the ground during the digging, it may be possible to save these in a similar container. Later the leader can help the children find pictures of them in books, and, depending upon the interest shown, enough time can be scheduled for studying them. Creatures found in this way, without advance planning, deserve their own class sessions and stories about their place in the interwoven web of life in the area where they are found. The teacher will have to judge whether the children's interest is only momentary, or if it deserves a side trip exploration of its own as part of their oncoming experiences in the world of living things.

Unless the children do so first, the leader provides the suggestion that earthworms found in the digging of soil go into jars of dirt where they can be fed and watched for a while. When questions follow: "Will they die if we put them in the jar?" or "What do they eat?" it is time to suggest looking in a book on earthworms back at the meeting place. Even though the leader knows the answer, it is better to offer the source than the information. Back in the classroom adult and children can seek the answers together. There may be time also, to label the bottles containing soil specimens and to look up the meaning of the word *humus*. After reading the definition the children may be able to answer the questions asked at the first session: "Do you know how soil is made?" "Is it still being made?" And if the reference material on earthworms has told the children what earthworms eat, someone is sure to be able to tell what kind of soil they would prefer to live in, finding a use right away for the new word *humus*.

After the children have had a chance to examine the different kinds of soil, the contents of all the bottles could be mixed together, one way of "making soil." If there is enough to fill a small flowerpot, a seed or two could be planted to test the fertility of a combination of clay, sand, and humus.

The story of how rocks are turned into soil by the action of heat, cold, air, water, sunlight, acid secreted by lichens, and other agents may come into the children's discussion; but unless it does, this detailed exploration of the sources of soil should be left for the future. Unless they have been led to feel "now I know all about it" this will remain an open-ended exploration to continue when they are older. If enough children obviously want to continue the study of soil for one more session, by all means let them do so; the single child showing interest can be supplied with a book to take home.

However, most of the boys and girls will be more interested in live earthworms, and "next week" becomes something to look forward to if a child knows he is to bring back his earthworm collection and that magnification will be possible at that time. After this second session on earthworms is held and the children have learned all they can by watching their specimens it may be time for reading the summarizing story. "The Earthworm."

OTHER POSSIBLE EXPERIENCES WITH EARTHWORMS

1. If some of the children are reluctant to handle the earthworms, the teacher can provide paper-covered drinking straws, and show them how to make "paper worms." If the paper is pushed down it comes off bunched in "accordion folds." Lay these folded papers in the children's hands, and add a few drops of water. The paper will expand in much the same way that an

earthworm crawls and accustom them to the feeling. Many will then be eager to hold a "real" earthworm and see if it feels the same or feels different.

2. When the children become restless with observation it is time for a little dramatic interlude. A series of chairs in a row will give a crawl space which can serve as a burrow, and the children can become the worms. After they have developed, thus, a feeling for earthworms, perhaps they will want to make up a poem or a song about how they think an earthworm feels.

3. If a jar is filled with clear-cut layers of the three types of soil — clay, sand in the middle, humus on the top, and some earthworms are put into this jar, observation after a few days will show the earthworm in his burrowing and crawling has mixed the soil. The observers will come to understand through this experience another contribution which the earthworm makes.

4. *Science and Children* gives this recipe for raising angleworms which may prove helpful if the class is interested in doing this:[1]

> Place one large pail of black dirt (with angleworms) in a large container.
> Every week add these ingredients:
> > ½ cup raw oatmeal
> > ½ cup or more of coffee grounds
> > 1 tablespoon of milk
>
> Scratch the ingredients into the dirt, and keep adding enough water to keep the mixture damp but not wet.

BOOKS FOR THE CHILDREN'S USE

Children's Books About Earthworms

> Hogner, Dorothy Childs. *Earthworms.* Crowell.
> Excellent material, well illustrated, and including instructions for raising earthworms.
>
> *Note:* This is the only book specific to earthworms we have found. The leader will want to use encyclopedias

1 Reprinted with permission from *Science and Children,* Volume 2, Number 2 (October 1964). "Salamanders and Angleworms" by Constance Odanvich. Copyright 1964 by the National Science Teachers Association, Washington, D.C. 20036.

for this subject, and also look in some of the more general books where there are occasional references to earthworms. However, the Hogner book is thorough and will probably satisfy the needs of the group.

SONGS AND POEMS TO USE

"Earth worm": page 91 in *Poems To Grow On.*

STORY TO SUMMARIZE THE EXPERIENCE

THE EARTHWORM

THE THREE TERRY CHILDREN were playing in the sandbox under the cherry tree in their backyard one summer day. They piled the sand into mountains, poured water into it to make rivers and lakes, dug tunnels through the mountains, and made roads for small cars. The youngest child, a boy named Alan, dug deep down until he found he was making a hole into the soil under the sand. This was a good idea because it showed him how different the dark dirt was from the light sand, and because he found an earthworm down there. From the earthworm, he and his sister and older brother learned something about their own backyard, something they hadn't known before.

When Alan Terry found the earthworm it was just coming up out of the ground. It was long and thin. It was covered with rather wet slippery red-brown skin. As Alan watched it move along, he saw that its body was made up of little rings all fastened together. He let the earthworm go wherever it wanted to while he was watching it. When it moved, the earthworm stretched out and drew up together again.

"It looks like it's made of rubber," said Alan's sister, Ann.

"I wonder if it can see," said the older boy, Tom. "There's nothing at the front end of it that looks like eyes."

The children knew their father had a strong magnifying glass that showed small things as though they were ten times larger than they really were. Perhaps he would let them use it. They decided to take the earthworm inside where Mr. Terry was working at his workbench. Although Alan was the youngest,

he carried the earthworm because he had been the one to discover it. He carried it carefully on a large leaf.

Mr. Terry admired the earthworm and then got his magnifying glass from a drawer in his desk. Through its strong lens
the children saw two rows of stiff hairs under the earthworm. It
used these hairs instead of legs. There was also a row of hairs on
each side that helped. The first hairs near the front of the worm
moved ahead and then stopped while the ones behind took turns
catching up. When the earthworm stretched out it was long and
thin, but when its front end stood still and the last rings came
up closer to the front ones, it was plump and shorter.

Tom couldn't find the eyes he was looking for. He said he
was going to get a library book on earthworms and find out how
they knew where to go if they had no eyes. Tom was old enough
to go to the library alone.

The earthworm began crawling out of the circle of light
that shone down on it from a light bulb hanging over the workbench.

"Don't let him get away," said Ann.

"Why don't you put your earthworm in a jar full of sand
and dirt?" suggested Mr. Terry. "Worms get weak if they get
too dry or too cold. See, right now it's trying to find a place
where the air isn't so hot as it is under this light. If you put it
into a jar full of soil it will burrow right down to a cooler moist
place and be comfortable."

"But then we can't see it," objected Alan.

"So you can't, but if you put enough worms into the jar
and it's made of glass, at least one is pretty sure to burrow near
the side of the jar where we can watch it."

Everyone helped. They dug up three more worms in the
garden. They wet the sand and dirt a little before filling the jar
so the earthworms would find it easy to wriggle down into the
dark moist place. Earthworms are made just right for burrowing.
At first it seemed Alan was right, they couldn't see the worms.
But a few hours later they found one was tunneling through the
soil near the side of the jar where they could watch him.

"Even if the ground is too hard to push aside, earthworms
can get through it," Mr. Terry told the children. "They can eat

their way through. The dirt goes in through their mouths at one end and comes out the other end, but first all the tiny bits of leaf or grass or other food in the dirt is digested to help the earthworm grow."

"We don't want these worms to starve," said Tom. "Let's put some leaves on top, and see whether they eat them."

"We don't want them to get out, either, when they come up for the leaves," said Ann. "If we make some holes in the jar lid, they can get air but they can't crawl out."

Alan thought of one more thing the worms would need. "A few drops of water every day to keep their dirt just right," he said. "We don't want too much or their tunnels will get filled with water, but we don't want it too dry, either."

After a few weeks the children forgot to sprinkle water on the dirt in the earthworm jar, and their father said it was time to put the worms back in the garden.

"We need them out there," he said. "Their burrows leave open spaces in the soil to hold water and air, and that helps the tiny roots of plants to grow."

Instead of leaves the children found piles of lumpy dirt on top of the earth in the jar.

"Sometimes I see little piles like that all over outdoors in the morning," said Alan.

"Earthworms are night creatures," said Tom. "I read in a library book that they stick out their heads at night and pull the pieces of food down into their burrows. Or they stick out their tails and get rid of the dirt they've eaten if they didn't have any leaves and stuff. Those piles of dirt are called 'castings.' They fertilize the soil."

"What's 'fertilize'?" asked Alan.

"Oh, it means they put things into the soil that plants need for growing, make it richer, better soil."

"And I found out too that earthworms have no eyes," Tom went on, enjoying himself because he had so much to tell Ann and Alan about earthworms. "But they have some tiny spots called 'cells' that can feel the difference between light and dark. That's all they need."

When the children emptied out the dirt and the four big

worms onto the ground they discovered some very tiny worms that had hatched during the time the earthworms had lived in the jar. They weren't much bigger than a pencil mark, but very wiggly.

"Cover the baby ones with soft dirt," said Ann. "They'll get big and help our garden grow."

It was a good thing the children put more earthworms back into the yard than they took out, because the vegetables planted there needed many of them, and so did the grass on the lawn, the trees, bushes, flowers, and all the plants. All had small roots pushing down in search of food and air and water. If the earthworms broke up the soil and kept it soft and full of tunnels the plants would find it much easier to grow.

Up in the cherry tree above the sandbox was another live thing that needed earthworms, a brown bird with a red breast and a yellow bill.

INTRODUCTION TO THE EXPERIENCE TO FOLLOW

After discussing the story or their experiences in the light of the story, those children willing to do so can turn their own worms back into the yard. Any who are reluctant can be allowed to keep them one more week if they remember to care for the worms. When these are brought to class after such a two- or three-week interval, it is possible that baby worms will be found. If none are found at either time, further digging in a likely place may yield at least one baby worm "not much bigger than a pencil mark, but very wiggly."

If another subject has been chosen for the next experience work out a natural introduction to it. If robins are to be studied the leader will start with some questions about earthworms and robins. Or the leader may move right in the direction of the robin by asking:

"Does a robin *see* the worm or *hear* it in the ground?"

"What else do robins eat?"

"How can you tell the mother and father robin apart?"

"What are robins doing right now at this time of year?"

"Do we want them to eat our earthworms?"

EXPERIENCE WITH

Robins

DEVELOPING THE EXPERIENCE

LAUNCHING A CLASS EXPERIENCE with robins will require differing methods according to the time of year it is undertaken. In fall and winter one can look for robins' nests which are no longer needed by the birds, and the experience can start with these. In spring one can be alert to find signs of nest building, and both in spring and summer one can be watching for activity on the part of the robins which clearly points to the fact that they are feeding a brood of young.

At the end of their breeding season robins flock by sexes, all males together and all females together, for migration. They have raised two broods in the course of the summer, and if they have had good luck with the two families the cock robin will come back to the same territory, arriving ahead of his mate. (A bird's territory, of course, is the area which he selects, presumably containing enough food of the kind he needs for the raising of a brood of young ones, and the feeding of himself and his mate.)

The robin defends his territory against all other male robins or other birds he considers enemies or food-rivals. He flies from one boundary mark to another, completing the circuit many times a day, singing loudly from each of his perches. When the robin's mate arrives (the one of the previous year, or, if she doesn't return, an unmated female in the flock of returning hen robins), she is the one to select the actual site for a nest.

The robin has a rich repertoire of songs. Singing to "declare territory" is only one use he makes of his singing ability.

Robins will fight an intruding enemy or food-rival fiercely. Occasionally they will even fight their own reflection in a window. There are seldom any casualties in an actual combat; one of the two seems to know when he is outmatched and gives in, altering the boundary he tried to set up by conceding the disputed tree or bush to the victor.

The building of a robin's nest is often easy to watch since they aren't averse to being near human dwellings. There will be no leaves in the nest as a rule, although other kinds of thrushes will use leaves. The male may not help with the nest building, nor share the job of sitting on the eggs, but he is an indefatigable guard.

Three or four "robin's egg blue" eggs are usually laid. Thirteen days are required for incubation. The robin lays one egg a day and doesn't stay on the eggs until all are laid, so the incubation period begins on the day the last egg is laid. In this way all hatch at the same time. By the time the newly hatched babies are ten days old, both robins are working from dawn to dark feeding the young ones.

Many people believe the robin listens for a worm's movement in the ground, but Dr. A. A. Allen, Cornell's famous ornithologist, says that the robin can see the tip of the angle worm protruding from its burrow if he cocks his head and looks closely with one eye only. It is hard to dislodge the worm, for its bristles can anchor it quite firmly. The robin also hunts for grubs, beetles, bugs, early cherries, and berries, preferring wild fruit if it is available: mulberries, dogwood berries, and wild grapes, for instance.

The parent birds inspect the nest after each feeding and remove from it the mucous sac containing the excreta of the infants. By the fifteenth day the young robins have strong enough wing feathers to support their heavy bodies pretty well. Now they are apt to leave the nest. There is a strong chance that all will not survive, for robins are beset by many predators. The strongest and the smartest ones may escape and they will soon be able to find their own food; whereupon the mother robin will build a second nest for a second brood.

If the robin story at the end of this experience is to be used in the spring, children can put out materials for the robin to find for nest making; strips of cloth, pieces of string or yarn, strips of paper. If class meeting places make it possible to watch the mother robin at work it will interest the children to see which of the materials are taken. Or they can be given these materials to take home unless they live in large city apartments. If most of the children are in apartment areas then a trip to a park is a real necessity.

If this study is made in fall or winter a search for an old nest in the trees now bare of leaves should provide the children with not only a robin's nest, but other kinds of nests to study and compare. As in the story, it would be interesting to take a nest apart and see what has been used in making it, and then the making of a similar nest can be undertaken. The teacher, while this activity is going on, will want to raise the question (if the children have not already done so) of how the robin knows how to build a nest. Why doesn't the robin build an oriole's nest? This gives a real opportunity for the discussion of the role of instinct; the robin "knows" without learning, he builds by instinct, and he always builds a robin's nest, not changing it to something else. Even quite small children can sense the wonder of this phenomenon of knowledge through instinct.

Hatching a fertile hen's egg in a small incubator is now possible in the classroom. Timing of the event is difficult, however, and it may be more satisfactory to arrange a visit to a hatchery if the children have never had the experience of watching a bird's egg hatch. Beautiful pictures and films of bird life are available through Audubon Society offices, as well as through many public libraries and university libraries.

Since a robin's song is so familiar children would enjoy identifying it from all the songs recorded on the various bird-call records and tapes offered by many libraries. By playing it over and over until the tune is familiar the children could write words for a class song about the robin.

In some parts of the country robins are among the birds that stay all winter. These are usually migrants from regions farther north or higher in altitude and not the same robins who will be breeding there in the summer. Although they will not be nesting they can be fed, photographed, sketched, and observed as individuals and in flocks.

The teacher will have to decide when the children have exhausted their interest in the robin and its nest building and the rearing of the young; when they have, they are ready to hear the story "The Robin," which will summarize their experiences and perhaps suggest a few new ones.

OTHER POSSIBLE EXPERIENCES WITH ROBINS

1. Use the story of the nest, not a robin's nest, in Edith F. Hunter's *Conversations with Children,* "The Snakeskin and the Carrot Bag" (Boston, Beacon Press, 1961).

2. Since the children will not have been able to "make" a very satisfactory robin's nest if they tried, it might relieve the frustration of that experience if they model a nest with clay, perhaps putting in the eggs and then making the father and mother robin as well.

3. Younger children certainly, and possibly all the children, would enjoy dramatizing the story. A pile of leaves or a blanket can be used for the nest, and the mother robin can sit on the eggs while the father flies around and protects his territory (he may even have an enemy or two to frighten off). Then three or four children can become the baby birds, while the mother and father fly around and make trip after trip back to the nest with food for the ever-hungry babies. Finally the mother can encourage the babies to try flying, and one by one they can all leave the nest, and hunt worms on the lawn. As is so often true with a dramatized story, this can easily be adapted from story form to dance form, and thus give the children another mode of expression as well as real satisfaction.

4. The teacher can collect pictures of many kinds of birds and birds' nests (*Arizona Highways* and *Natural History* are two

magazines which are rich sources of such pictures). Perhaps from this there can grow at least a limited experience in bird watching and bird identification, which for so many adults becomes a source of lifelong interest. They might draw pictures on a chart of all the birds they see on a field trip to the park or to the country. A "bird watcher" from among the adults known to the group would be a tremendous help on such a trip, so that the children can know what they are seeing. Such a trip is often more rewarding when the leaves are off the trees, for then the birds are so much easier to see.

5. Children need some experience in careful observation, and this might be a good opportunity for such experience. They can sit quietly on the lawn and watch to see just how the robin hops, how he cocks his head, how he bends down, and so forth. Again having watched, the children may want to express the experience as a dance.

6. Using the book *Robins on the Window Sill* (see list which follows) it might be good to spend a session discussing further the life cycle of the robin.

7. Another possibility, since one cannot "collect birds," would be to start a feather collection. There are suggestions for doing this in *If I Were a Bird* (see list which follows).

BOOKS FOR THE CHILDREN'S USE

Children's Books About Robins

> Eberle, Irmengarde. *Robins on the Window Sill*. Crowell.
> Particularly valuable for photographs, which are beautiful. The teacher will want to "narrate" for herself, as the text is dull.
> Flack, Marjorie. *Restless Robin*. Houghton.
> A classic story of an American robin, his migration, and the arrival of his mate, and then the raising of the birds.
> Simon, Norma. *Benjy's Bird*. Whitman.
> Experiences with a pet robin, including the final parting.

Varley, Dimitry. *The Whirly Bird*. Knopf.
Based on an actual experience, this is a story about the care given by a little girl to an injured baby bird and about the problems related to the bird's learning to fly.

Children's Books About Birds in General
(many including robins)

Bosiger, E., and Guilcher, J. M. *A Bird Is Born*. Sterling.
Fascinating photographs, including a series showing embryonic development; teacher will want to look at this with child to interpret and answer questions.

Bridgman, Betty. *Lullaby For Eggs*. Macmillan.
A lovely lullaby, without music, for all the eggs in nests everywhere.

Conklin, Gladys. *If I Were a Bird*. Holiday.
Songs, calls, and characteristics of common birds. Musical notes for easily recognized songs. Suggestions for a feather collection.

Fox, Charles P. *Birds Will Come to You*. Reilley & Lee.
How to attract and feed birds, how to build birdhouses. A book that will stimulate many interests.

Gans, Roma. *Birds Eat and Eat and Eat*. Crowell.
Simple and factual, but useful for its easy reading level.

Gans, Roma. *It's Nesting Time*. Crowell.
Easy reading, clear, and useful for its drawings.

Headstrom, Richard. *Birds' Nests: A Field Guide*. Washburn (David McKay Co., Inc.).
Excellent guide, with many pictures. Although an adult book the leader may use it with the children. Birds' nests are difficult to identify at best.

Shackelford, Nina, and Burks, Gordon. *Bird Nests*. Golden Press.
Does not compare with Headstrom (above), but the pictures are bright and clear and will have appeal for browsing.

SONGS AND POEMS TO USE

"Of Speckled Eggs the Birdie Sings": Number 85 in *We Sing of Life*.

"Robin in the Garden": page 96 in *Poems To Grow On*.

THE ROBIN

A MOTHER ROBIN was building her nest in the tree above the children's sandbox. She was not as handsome as her mate, who had a blacker head and a redder breast with a touch of white at his throat, but she was a very hard worker. She tucked in the ends of long grasses and fastened them with mud, then flew to get more, stopping only when she was quite tired and hungry to join her mate on the ground.

The Terry children often watched the robins hop along near each other, their heads cocked so one eye was always looking down. Every little while they thrust sharp beaks into the dirt and pulled out worms and ate them. Earthworms seemed to be their favorite meat. A lunch of earthworms made the mother robin strong enough to go on with her work of building the nest.

Ann didn't like this. She said, "I wish they wouldn't eat our earthworms!"

She went to tell her father what was happening. "You said we need the earthworms in our yard, but now the robins are eating them."

Mr. Terry explained to her that the robin's lunch was a good thing.

"If there were no birds or other animals to eat earthworms, all the new baby ones would keep hatching and growing big enough to lay eggs and hatch *more* baby ones and soon the ground would be so closely packed with earthworms there wouldn't be food enough for them all. If they had no food they would die. So earthworms need robins," he said.

When the children thought about this they were still not sure they were glad that robins liked earthworms for meat.

"I'm sure earthworms don't *like* to be eaten," said Ann.

Each day Alan watched the nest grow while he played in the sand below the tree. He was the one who noticed that the mother robin was the only one building the nest. He could tell because her face got so dirty from carrying mud. She seemed to be using dried grass and mud, a few pieces of string, and one long strip of something that looked like paper or a piece of cloth. After she added mud from her bill, she always turned around and around in the nest to keep the wet mud shaped like a bowl inside. After several days she seemed to think her work was done. She filled the bowl with soft, clean grass and settled down inside it.

Alan wished he knew how many eggs she laid inside the nest. Later he learned there had been four of them, bluish green and very pretty. She kept them covered all the time under her warm feathery body, except for a few minutes once in a while when she flew away for a drink of water or a restful stretch of her wings. The father robin often brought her food, and he watched the nest whenever she left it, but he didn't sit on the eggs. He guarded them well, scolding any person or animal that came near.

Even before the eggs were laid the father robin had been chasing away other birds whom he didn't want living too near his nest. It was just as if he was screaming at them, "Our family needs all the worms and bugs and cherries in this yard. You go farther away and find your own food. This is our hunting ground!"

Alan thought he was a very cross robin. But when the eggs had hatched and both parent robins were busy *all* day *every* day finding food for their growing babies, he understood why the father had protected his own territory this way. It took all the worms and bugs the mother and father could find to help their little fluffy babies grow into large robins with feathers and with wings strong enough to fly.

When the four young robins were learning to fly, the children tried to keep their cat in the house during the day as much as they could. When she did get into the yard the mother and father robin scolded and flew down like dive-bombers trying to scare her away.

Soon there were six fat robins hopping around in the green grass of the lawn eating earthworms and grasshoppers, beetles and bugs. The babies were as large as their parents, but they had speckled breasts instead of red ones, and they ate more food.

This was a good thing for the garden because some of the insects they ate were harmful to plants. And it was a good thing for everyone in the neighborhood to hear the robins singing. When Alan, Ann, Tom, and their big brother, Jim, and Mr. and Mrs. Terry woke up in the morning the robin's song was the first thing they heard. The children liked to hear those cheery warbles at bedtime, too, just as they were closing their eyes.

One day after the robins had gone south for the winter the children decided to make nests like the empty one in the cherry tree. They used all the same materials, and it was fun, but it wasn't easy. Mrs. Terry tried to make one too.

Although they had two hands to work with instead of one small bill, their nests didn't turn out to be as neat as the one the robin made. In fact their nests weren't neat at all!

"I'm sure no robin would be satisfied with this one," said Tom after his was finished. "How do they ever know how to do it so well, I wonder."

"The wonderful thing is that they are born knowing how," said Mrs. Terry. "But we would have to learn by watching them. Let's notice more carefully next spring just how the mother does it."

Someone else in the family would be noticing the robins next spring too. Mrs. Cat! But for a different reason.

INTRODUCTION TO THE EXPERIENCE TO FOLLOW

After the story about the robins and their experiences, the children may want to discuss further the question, "Do we want robins to eat our earthworms?" Of course this question may have been discussed the first time it was brought up at the close of the second experience. If they wish to talk about cats and robins right away, it might be a good time to bring the session to an end with more questions, this time about cats.

"How many kinds of cats are there, wild and tame?"

"Why do we like cats for pets?"

"Do we need cats?"

"Do birds need cats?"

"Can we learn some things we don't know about cats, as we have about earthworms and robins?"

"Would you like to have a farmer tell us what he thinks about cats?"

EXPERIENCE WITH

The Cat

DEVELOPING THE EXPERIENCE

WHEN THE CAT was domesticated and became a pet as well as a practical asset to the household, man had interfered with the balance of nature, as he would again and again. This time he put under his protection, against its natural enemies, one of the most effective predators in existence. When Cat was adopted, Man said in effect, "You keep the rodents away and I'll take care of you." If, later, man became fond of other wild creatures and began to recognize the usefulness as well as the appeal of birds, it was too late to revise the contract. He couldn't train this hunter to seek only the prey that was an "enemy" of man.

Today every child has to be torn between his feelings for the cat he loves and the birds toward whom his interest and wonder have been directed by his favorite adults. This problem exists for grown people as well as children, and when cat-lover and bird-lover live in the same neighborhood it may be quite futile to expect reason to rule over controversy.

Perhaps a feeling of guilt about the situation will always send those who love cats running to the yard to attempt the rescue of a threatened bird, even though they understand that a natural enemy is essential to the eventual welfare of the race upon which it preys. Because modern man protects the cat from its natural enemies, even to the extent of medical expense, he can only try also to protect the birds from his pet.

How unpredictable we must seem to cats! Something alive of the right size moves; the cat catches it skillfully and brings it home for praise only to be punished as often as he is rewarded.

Since the new experience has to do with a domestic animal and a pet, less time needs to be spent on exploring what cats do and how they live than in the case of the earthworm or the grasshopper. Children know so much already about cats. However, they can greatly enjoy some experiences we have to suggest, and may be learning to look at a familiar pet in a new and different way.

Should Halloween be near, the myth about witch's cats can be studied in a way that will help the children to understand how myths develop, and incidentally clarify the subject of witches for those still young enough to have fears engendered by too early exposure to fairy-tale movies and stories of witches. Wilfred S. Bronson, in his excellent book *Cats,* suggests in a cartoon the following background to the whole idea of the witch's black cat:

When a little black cat, improperly fed and cared for, had a "fit," ignorant owners once thought it to be "bewitched" by some magical evil spirit. Now they could think of many mysterious things about black cats. At night, outdoors, black cats disappear and appear suddenly. (Why?) Even indoors they can turn up right beside you when you didn't know they were near. (Padded paws.) And they can see in the dark! (How? See below.) When you stroke them, what are those sparks they give off? Why do cats get together and scream such terrible sounds at each other sometimes? (The cat's way of attracting a mate and terrifying his rivals: like the robin's song!) And cats aren't even afraid of haunted houses! (They aren't silly enough to think a house *can* be haunted by anything except rats and mice, and that makes an old house attractive instead of scary to a cat.) Oh, yes, someone had seen a lonely old woman talking to her black cat as she stirred her evening meal over the fire, and the cat looked as if it understood what she was saying! (Cats look right into our eyes, unlike dogs, and enjoy being talked to. Like babies, they seldom blink, which gives them a "wise" expression as though they can read our thoughts.) It makes some people feel very "good" if they imagine that someone else is very "bad," and it is easier to think of an ugly person as being wicked. (A poor old woman who has no one to take care of her may not look very pretty. Why?) Then, suppose her neighbor's chickens all died of a disease contagious to chickens, but not recognized at that time and therefore mysterious. "Of course!" the people said. "The old woman must be a witch. Maybe she fed them that magic potion we saw her stirring while she talked to her black cat."

A Halloween party is a fine time to cook good food over a fire while working out such a myth-beginning, and later it could be acted out as an impromptu play. The origin of superstition is interesting to children, and they may have other questions to ask about cats or other creatures in this area.

In discovering how cats are adapted to their way of life children can watch a cat use its whiskers to measure the width of a passageway through which it is going for the first time. In this way it makes sure that it won't get stuck in a place too tight for the rest of the body to clear.

If the room is darkened, they can observe how wide the cat's pupils become to admit as much light as possible. (With a flashlight they can see how their own pupils change size when going from dark to light.) Since the muscles controlling the amount of light that reaches the cat's eyes are very similar to the "shutters" which do the same service for a camera lens, a picture taken in dim light can help make the process more understandable to children, who will also enjoy opening and closing the lens diaphragm of an empty camera. When the light goes through the lens of the cat's eye it is reflected back so that it seems to "glow." If there were a mirror behind the film in the camera it would also seem to glow in the dark.

Children may be able to think of the reasons for some of the cat's other physical characteristics. Why do they wash so carefully after eating? (Clean fur gives off no odor to warn the mice.) Why are the feet padded and the claws retractable? Why does the tongue have a rough surface?

Whenever there is talk about cats, mice are mentioned as their prey. Since our children are brought up on stories about lovable mouse characters, it is as easy for them to identify with the mouse as with the cat. Although families often keep a cat because they consider mice all right *out*doors, but not wanted indoors for good reasons, so many houses are mouseproof by construction today that some boys and girls may never see any mice except the ones their own cat brings home. This makes it hard for them to think that cats keep mice away! The farmer's point of view may be new to them. He is apt to inform them about the rapidity with which mice multiply. If there are no cats, owls, or other rodent-eating animals about, a farmer's grain can be depleted and other problems created by rats and mice. If the class can visit a farm, one where the farmer is intelligently informed on the subject of predators as well as mice, this can give a new picture of the cat to children who have always been on the side of the smaller mouse.

Another experience is easiest to carry through if a zoo is available, yet can be satisfactory if one has to use pictures and books. This is the recognition of the relationship between the domestic cat and the other forty-odd members of the cat family including lions, tigers, leopards, lynxes, bobcats, cheetahs, ocelots, pumas, and cougars. Likeness and differences can be observed and discussed, and then reproduced in drawings and paintings. Do these cats also have importance in the places where they live wild, as cats have importance in our neighborhoods?

After watching cats at play, boys and girls can enjoy imitating them to appropriate music, pretending to hunt silently for food, following a string around the room, or batting at a paper tied to the end of it which is swung for them. This play can easily grow into a "cat dance" which the children will enjoy.

OTHER POSSIBLE EXPERIENCES WITH CATS

1. If possible a mother cat and her kittens should be brought into the classroom for observation of kittens nursing, running, and tumbling. The children can play "cat games" with them. If no one has such a cat to offer, it is often possible to borrow one

for the day from the Animal Rescue League, local Humane Society, or Society for the Prevention of Cruelty to Animals. (If the children want the kittens, none should be given away until they are old enough to be taken from the mother, nor until the child has brought written permission from home.)

2. After watching kittens trying to drink from a saucer, many of the children would like to try to do this. They have wanted to do as much at home in many cases. This will show them that it is not as easy as it looks, and help them find one answer to the usefulness of the cat's rough tongue.

3. It is interesting to try feeding the kittens with a medicine dropper; even a very young kitten will be able to drink from it with a little practice. They can adapt somewhat to their environment, as this will show, and they can learn something new.

4. By observing the behavior of the mother cat with her babies the children will see that she is teaching them things: that she slaps at them, scolds with her voice, and so forth. Cats are not born knowing everything they are ever going to know, even though there are some things that they seem to do without learning (that is, by instinct). For instance, a cat generally knows how to teach her babies.

5. Use Kate Seredy's book *Gypsy* (see list which follows) to expand the cat story into a session on the life cycle. One cannot stress the life cycle too often. This is one of the best of the life-cycle books: realistic, beautiful, and appealing to the children.

6. If the children get restless at any point it might be a good time to let them play the familiar game of "Cat and Mice." They might like to speculate as to how this game was invented. Origins are always worth considering, even when we know definitive answers cannot be found.

BOOKS FOR THE CHILDREN'S USE

Children's Books About Cats

> Beebe, B. F. *American Lions and Cats*. McKay.
> This book was appraised by *Natural History* with the comment "none better."

Birnbaum, A. *Green Eyes*. Capitol (Golden Press).

A simple story of the growth of Green Eyes from being "very little" to a year old. His birth, however, is avoided.

Bronson, Wilfred S. *Cats*. Harcourt.

This contains the material mentioned on witch's cats, and much other material which will add interest to discussion.

Paull, Grace. *Freddy the Curious Cat*. Doubleday.

Long a favorite cat story of children.

Seredy, Kate. *Gypsy*. Viking.

A truly beautiful and important book. Includes the whole life cycle, and the excitement and dangers of the world of the cat.

Zim, Herbert. *The Big Cats*. Morrow.

Not so outstanding as the Beebe book, but a wealth of information and pictures.

SONGS AND POEMS TO USE

"Tiger-Cat Tim": page 104 in *Poems To Grow On*.
"Cat": page 105 in *Poems To Grow On*.

STORY TO SUMMARIZE THE EXPERIENCE

THE CAT

Mrs. Cat had golden fur and beautiful yellow eyes. When she was inside the house she was a soft, warm, purring pussy. She enjoyed playing with a little ball that rolled away from her paw when she pushed it. As it ran ahead of her she chased it all over the house, under chairs and tables, batting it with a quick motion whenever she reached it so it continued to roll. If Alan or Ann or Tom pulled a string along the floor in front of her, Mrs. Cat went dancing after it, tumbling and jumping as she tried to catch the end with her teeth. Nothing made Mrs. Cat happier, however, than being allowed to sit on a friendly lap, curled up in a contented ball while a gentle hand smoothed her silky fur.

When Mrs. Cat had a family of four baby kittens, she was a good mother. She washed her little ones with her rough pink tongue and kept them clean and fluffy. She gave them her own milk when they were tiny, and when they were larger taught them how to drink cow's milk from a saucer. When the kittens were old enough for meat she showed them how to chew it, and how to growl if another cat tried to take it away from them.

Mrs. Cat was well behaved and greatly loved by everyone in the family when she was inside the house, where she liked to stay most of the day. However, at night she stayed outdoors.

It was surprising to see the change in Mrs. Cat when she went outdoors at night. First she stopped and sniffed the evening air and listened for sounds as she looked all around. When she walked through the garden she moved with a low, stretched-out, slinky look, much like a leopard in the jungle. She crouched close to the ground so the plants would hide her, because now Mrs. Cat had begun the exciting part of her life. She was being a hunter, and she seemed to know that larger animals might be hunting *her*. She wasn't playing. Mrs. Cat was doing her best to catch something alive, even though she wasn't hungry. She did this because hunting is something all cats, large jungle cats and small house cats, enjoy most of all. It is their business, especially when they are outdoors and at night.

Mrs. Cat often caught a mouse, a mole, or even a rat, chipmunk, or small squirrel. She didn't always eat the animals she caught. Often she tossed her prize around, playing with it the same way she played with her ball in the house. A quick, clever little mouse could sometimes get away during this game without being hurt at all. Usually, Mrs. Cat carried her captive home before she played with it. The children often found little dead mice or moles lying on the porch in the morning.

Everyone in Mrs. Cat's house tried to keep her inside all day while the baby robins were learning to fly. This worked very well while the robins were raising their first family, but later in the summer they had a second brood. There were three babies in the second family. One of them didn't do as well at flying as the others. He had never been as large as the other two, who often managed to crowd him aside when the parent birds were feeding them an earthworm. They grew faster than he, because they got more to eat, and therefore their wings were stronger.

During the flying lessons two of the young birds were able to flutter high enough to keep away from Mrs. Cat when she suddenly appeared on the lawn. But the one who seemed to be weaker than the others was too slow. In one quick leap, Mrs. Cat caught the little bird and killed it.

"Don't," screamed the children, running toward her. "Bad Mrs. Cat. Bad, bad cat! Let that little bird go." But the young robin's life was already gone. All that was left was his small body, mostly feathers.

"He's dead, Daddy!" Ann was crying as she went to her father for comfort.

Alan watched Mrs. Cat run off into the garden with the dinner she had caught, growling as she taught her kittens to do if anyone tried to take their meat.

Mrs. Terry and Jim, the big brother who went to high school, came out on the back porch to see what was happening. Mr. Terry was stroking Ann's hair while he talked to her.

"I know how you feel," he said. "We all wanted to help the little robin get away. But he wasn't as strong as the others. Perhaps he wasn't strong enough to live very long anyway."

Jim joined the younger children and told them something he had learned at school. "You know a weak, sickly bird can get a disease that is catching, and give it to his whole family so they all die. There aren't any doctors to cure sickness for wild birds. Perhaps that time Mrs. Cat was doing the other robins a favor."

"Yes, but sometimes Mrs. Cat catches *well* birds, too," said Alan. "All the birds just hate her."

"That's right," said Jim. "But they don't know she kills some of their enemies too, rats and chipmunks and squirrels who like to eat birds' eggs. She helps the birds in several ways, but they don't know it. When you think about it, the birds really need Mrs. Cat."

Tom had been thinking. "I guess she isn't so bad," he said. "You know we eat birds, too, and eggs. I guess she's just doing what a cat does, and we're just doing what people do."

Mrs. Terry spoke up as they all went back into the house together. "Mrs. Cat really does a good job of being a cat," she said. "We want her to keep mice out of the house, and she does. I do wish she would leave the birds alone, but she *is* needed in this place. Just as the birds and the earthworms are needed. Everything alive needs all the other living things."

Before Alan, Ann and Tom went to sleep that night they tried to say this to each other, and they found it made a poem, almost a song.

> Worms need plants, plants need worms,
> Birds need worms, worms need birds,
> Cats need birds, birds need cats.
> Living things need each other.

As they learned more about the live things in their backyard, this song got longer and longer. Sometimes they sang it as they played in the sandbox under the cherry tree, and the tree was a part of the song — the tree the robin had needed for her nest.

INTRODUCTION TO THE EXPERIENCE TO FOLLOW

In our story "Mrs. Cat," a chant is begun something like "The House That Jack Built" which is to become more complicated with each experience through the year. Now the interdependence of all living things begins to become apparent. Since the story ends with this chant, the teacher can appropriately look out the window after the line "living things need each other" has been read, and if a tree is visible she can ask, "What do you see that is alive out there?"

After someone recognizes the tree as something alive, it is natural for the suggestion to be made, "Can we try next week to discover what other living things need trees and what trees need in order to live? Dress for an outdoor exploration." In this way expectation can be directed toward the fifth experience.

A Tree

DEVELOPING THE EXPERIENCE

MANKIND AND TREES have a spiritual relationship almost as close and as ancient as mankind and the sea. It has been said that life began in the sea and man began in the trees. From the need to hold its branches, came the hand. It is probable that the tree also gave us fire. It is no wonder that early man worshipped trees. Tree mythology is a rich source of knowledge about our early ancestors, and any adult undertaking the leadership of a tree adventure-study will do well to dip into its pages as well as reading books on the ecology of trees.

Trees have been likened to ministers of the government of Nature. If the benign influence of the forest is lost, deserts, floods, suffering, and dying civilizations follow.

In many classrooms and books for years to come the kindergarten or primary children of today will learn about the varied uses of trees by man, the amazing variety of trees in the world, and how to recognize them. It is desirable that the present experience be principally with an individual tree, "adopted" by the class. If they come to call it "our tree," imitate it in dramatic play as it moves in the wind, listen to it, feel it, and have a feeling about it, their interest in the whole subject of trees may continue as a vital and intelligent one.

When the exploring children discuss what tree they want to

study, the list from which they make their choice should include one fruit tree. It is almost inevitable that the greatest number will prefer an apple or a cherry tree to others on the list. Whatever their choice, a good way to start the exploring is by seeing how many living things they can find that are using the tree in one way or another. This will involve the use of magnifying glasses, peering under bark, spending as much time as possible under or in the tree — really getting to know it.

If the tree is in bloom (and *all* trees do have flowers), a movie or film strip to show blossoms opening and bees or butterflies sipping nectar will help the children see what happens too high to be observed from the ground.

(If the children are tempted to stop for inquiry into the details of every new creature discovered making use of the tree, attention will go back to the tree itself if they are promised a time for future study of these other subjects. Time should be taken for their identification, however, so they can be listed for future inquiry.)

If the fruit is ripe, or can be found in the market, cutting it open, examining, and eating it will lead to discussion of what other living things enjoy this same fruit. There can be cooking adventures involved in this, too. The seeds will be discovered in the course of opening the fruit, and can eventually be planted either outside or in containers in the classroom. "How would they be planted if we didn't take the fruit?" opens another kind of inquiry.

Although some experiences depend upon the time of year, at any time a rope swing can be hung from a strong branch, knotted at the end, and used by the children as they swing in turn, jumping on and propelling themselves. Climbing into the tree will be even better if it lends itself to safe use in this way.

After such experiences the children will know the bark and leaves and shape of this tree well enough to enjoy recognizing them if bark, leaves, and pictures of several different trees are laid out on a table for them. In winter this "test" can include buds in place of leaves.

After everyone knows the shape of the tree above the ground, it is time to think of what lies below it. A forester or professional nursery man can trace on the ground the extent of the reaching roots below and help the children realize how deep they go. If a very large sheet of paper is spread over a table, the children can all work at the same time on drawing an entire tree, some working on the trunk and branches and some on the network of roots. Felt pens or dark crayons of large size will be most effective for such a picture.

OTHER POSSIBLE EXPERIENCES WITH A TREE

1. For West Coast children it will be possible to get redwood burls, which grow quite rapidly into lovely fernlike leaves, and make a dramatic setting for displays of various kinds. Except when there is danger of freezing in the mail these can also be ordered for other parts of the country and serve to introduce an unfamiliar tree. One may be ordered from Muir Woods Inn, Rt. 1, Box 151, Mill Valley, California, for $2.25.

2. Avocado seeds take a long time to sprout (unless you are lucky enough to find one in an avocado already starting to grow), but they contrast well with the small size of the cherry, or the very small seeds of the apple or pear. It would be interesting to collect a large number of fruit seeds and compare the seed with the size of the fruit, to discover that there is no direct relationship.

3. In the late summer and early fall, little tree sprouts, just coming up from seeds, can be found, especially under oak and maple, but also under many evergreens. If these are dug up with care they will often live for a long time, and are fascinating to the children as "baby trees" which indeed they are.

4. Many children (and some adults) do not realize that all trees have blossoms, so if it is spring it would be interesting to go hunting for them, and to look at them under 10x magnification. Under these circumstances the beauty of these flowers is often a great surprise.

5. A lumber yard can be the source of specimens of varying kinds of wood. When sandpapered (which children love to do) each will show the grain of the wood. A little oil stain rubbed on will bring the grain out more clearly. If they have not been oiled

prints can be made from the samples, particularly before they are sandpapered completely, and some of these will make fascinating over-all designs. Ends of pieces of lumber if smoothed a little can be used to block print the actual "living design" of the wood onto paper. In this way children can decorate plain-colored construction or tissue paper with the "tree's own design," and in the process carry their acquaintance with trees further.

6. If some of the children do not think it is possible for liquid to be drawn up by the tree one can always use the dramatic demonstration of a stalk of celery (or a white carnation, or lily-of-the-valley) which is set into colored ink. Soon the veins will show clearly as the ink is drawn up into the stem and into the blossom. This is something which children never seem to tire of seeing.

7. Should the interest carry over into other kinds of trees, and if the time of the year is right, either blue prints, or the easier spatter prints, of leaves can be made. The various evergreens are often quite lovely in a spatter print.

BOOKS FOR THE CHILDREN'S USE

Children's Books About Trees

> Bulla, Clyde R. *A Tree Is a Plant.* Crowell.
>> An apple tree is followed through the seasons from seed to bearing tree. Well done.
> Cormack, Maribelle. *The First Book of Trees.* Watts.
>> Adequately presents a good deal of material, but does not compare with the others on the list.
> Darby, Gene. *What Is a Tree?* Benefic. (out of print)
>> Easy reading, and gives a complete story of trees.
> George, Jean. *The Hole in the Tree.* Dutton.
>> A delightful book showing the succession of inhabitants as a hole in the tree becomes larger and larger.
> Guilcher, J. M., and Noailles, R. H. *A Tree Is Born.* Sterling.
>> One of the best. Superior and fascinating photographs which include close-ups and magnifications of the growth and parts of four familiar trees. A must!
> Selsam, Millicent. *Birth of a Forest.* Harper.
>> Carries the experience beyond the single tree of the

yard; clear drawings and excellent photographs make this useful for all ages though more difficult reading than some books on this list.

Sterling, Dorothy. *Trees and Their Story*. Doubleday.
Unusual photographic presentation of trees and how they live. Text for better readers, pictures for everyone.

Udry, Janice. *A Tree Is Nice*. Harper.
Simple, but helps to establish the relation to a single tree, which is the aim also of this experience with the apple tree.

Weaver, Harriet. *There Stand the Giants: The Story of the Redwood Trees*. Lane (Menlo Park, Calif.).
If the experience with redwood burls is used this book will be most useful. For all children it will be fascinating as well.

Adult Books About Trees

Boyle, E. Marie. *The Leafy Home of the Birds*. Beacon Science Series.
This is a study of trees written by a biologist and planned for an eight-week unit for grades three to five. Many suggested activities.

Collis, J. S. *The Triumph of the Tree*. Viking. Explorer Books X-3.
A most exciting book which will help any adult develop an enthusiasm for trees and will add a dimension to the experiences of the children which might not otherwise occur.

SONGS AND POEMS TO USE

"Johnny Appleseed": Number 54 in *We Sing of Life*.
"Leaves": Number 135 in *We Sing of Life*.
"In a Tree": page 67 in *Poems To Grow On*.
"Trees": page 68 in *Poems To Grow On*.
"Leaves Talking": Number 13 in *Martin and Judy Songs*.

STORY TO SUMMARIZE THE EXPERIENCE

THE CHERRY TREE

THE TREE above the Terrys' sandbox was a cherry tree. In the spring it turned into a giant bouquet of white flowers, when the small dark buds suddenly opened all over its bare branches. The bees and butterflies found sweet food in the blossoms, often before there were many other flowers to feed them.

By the time the petals had fallen into the sandbox making the ground all around the tree look as if a snowstorm had visited the backyard, new leaves had replaced the blossoms and the tree was green overhead instead of white.

The children noticed that grass didn't grow as well under the tree as it did everywhere else on the lawn.

"It's because we play here so much," Alan said.

"It's because grass likes sunshine," said their mother, "and of course it's shady under the tree."

"It's because grass roots need water," said Tom, "and all the water in the ground under the tree is going up into its branches."

Alan liked to stand close to the tree and feel its smooth bark cover, broken by rough cracks and ridges here and there. Underneath he knew water was going up into the tree. It made him wish the bark was glass so he could see inside.

The cherry tree was a busy place. Flying insects and crawling insects, birds and squirrels and cats and children used its branches. It wasn't an easy tree for boys and girls to climb, but Jim, who was almost grown up, had climbed high enough to hang a rope from one strong branch. There was a knot at the end of the rope so the children could stand on it and swing.

Alan could see all the activity outside the tree, but he couldn't see the water moving up inside carrying food-making materials out of the ground so the tree could grow and the little hard green cherries could swell into sweet red fruit. There was a cherry nearly every place where there had been a blossom in the early spring.

"What happens to the water?" Alan asked his father one hot July day. His father was cutting the grass not far from the sandbox. "I mean the water inside the cherry tree. Where does it go when it gets to the end of the branches?"

"We use a big word to describe that," said his father. "We say that the tree *transpires*. This means the water evaporates out through the plant tissue. It's a little like the way your skin sweats on a hot day, but not just the same. The air around the tree is full of moisture coming out from the leaves. Of course you can't see it, but it's there."

Alan found this a little hard to understand, and hard to believe — that the tree gave out water into the air as well as sucking it up from deep in the ground. But he told Ann anyway.

"A tree is like a fountain, only you can't see the water coming out," was the way he said it.

When the cherries were ripe Mr. Terry climbed a ladder to pick them. He complained while he worked above the children's heads.

"We won't get many of these cherries," he said. "The birds got here first, and either raccoons or big boys have been in this tree, too. We'll be lucky if we get a half-dozen cherry pies from what they have left."

"Cherries are popular," said Ann, who was playing in the sandbox. "I found a cherry in my doll teapot down here. Maybe a bird dropped it."

"I expect birds have been planting cherry trees all over this neighborhood by dropping the seeds when they eat the cherries," her father remarked.

Ann thought about the baby trees growing up. She knew the birds dropped the seeds far from the tree. Was it good or bad for a baby tree to grow up far from its parent? Of course the baby tree wouldn't know, but it might have a better chance of growing tall if it weren't right under a big tree, she decided. Probably trees really needed birds to plant the seeds.

"Trees need birds, birds need trees," became part of the "Needing Song." But the children hadn't discovered yet all the living things that the tree needed, nor all the living things that needed the tree.

Little mice found some of the cherry seeds that the birds had dropped. The mice hid them away for winter food.

After the cherries were gone summer went swiftly by. In the fall the leaves began to drop from the tree into the sandbox. All the children helped Mr. Terry rake leaves from the lawn. He told them they could play in the leaves and they did. They made houses with many rooms. Finally they helped their father pile leaves around the vines and bushes that grew close to the house.

Mr. Terry also used leaves to cover some of the plants in the vegetable garden so the ground wouldn't get too dry. They saved one pile of leaves for a bonfire, and as they sat around it Mother told them a little story:

"Out in the forest, where the trees keep the cold wind away and leaves cover the ground all winter, it sometimes doesn't freeze under the snow. As the snow melts on top of the dead leaves, the water can run down and soak into the ground. When spring comes the whole forest has water to spare. No one has to use a hose to wet the soil there. Springs bubble up and make rivers from the water stored under the ground."

"And we get the water from the rivers," added Tom. "It's all because of the trees in the forest. I learned that at school."

Although the cherry tree rested, after its next year's buds had formed, it was still offering food to a noisy little neighbor whom the children had come to know during the summer. And in the cracks of its bark it offered shelter through the freezing weather to other small living things.

INTRODUCTION TO THE EXPERIENCE TO FOLLOW

An ideal transition from this experience to the next one can follow if some tree authority can come in and tell the children in simple but dramatic fashion what a great unwitting service woodpeckers do in the protection of forests. Children fortunate enough to live near a state or national forest may have this experience at the forester's headquarters, or he may come to them. Or the leader may tell the story as the children sit around their tree.

Briefly, this is an example of how it can be told if no forester is available:

"In the western pine and spruce forests, bark beetles live all the year round. They don't like the sap of young, strong trees that are growing fast; something about it makes them avoid these trees. They attack the older ones whose growth is slowing. But in the same forests are many woodpeckers. They are hungry for bark beetles, and eat enough of them so the damage to the forest trees isn't too great. The way this can be proved is a very sad way. If a bad windstorm blows down many of the trees so their roots are still in the ground, loosened but able to keep the tree weakly alive as it lies on its side in the forest undergrowth, woodpeckers can reach only half of the tree to feed on the bark beetles — the half that isn't covered by grass, ferns, and other plants. So half of the bark beetles are able to live and raise families, and soon there are so many that they attack even the young strong trees and the entire forest may be killed in a few years because the woodpeckers can't control the beetles. The balance of nature has been upset."

If any of the children don't understand the meaning of balance it can be neatly demonstrated with a teeter-totter or a balancing scale, and the idea of nature's balance dramatized.

When the children's interest in their tree is at its height and the story "The Cherry Tree" has been read, the teacher will see that its closing paragraph has a reference to a "noisy little neighbor" fed by the tree in winter.

The leader can ask:

"What winter birds are noisy?"

"Where can we find them?"

"What do birds eat in winter?"

"What birds eat bark beetles?"

"Would you like to make a present for them the next time we meet?"

The Woodpecker

DEVELOPING THE EXPERIENCE

WOODPECKERS are found in nearly every part of the world. Even in treeless areas, where there is no wood to peck, woodpeckers are found nesting on the ground or in it, finding their insect food in the air or in the foliage of whatever plants thrive there.

Since there is, of course, no bird properly called by the simple name of "woodpecker," each genus having its own name, teachers should always properly identify the ones found locally so the children will know them by their correct names. Better still, with the aid of colored pictures and a field guide, the children can find out for themselves which kind of woodpecker they have been watching. The same holds true for flickers, among the most interesting of woodpeckers. Each section where the flicker is found has its own variety with its own name.

Winter study of the woodpecker family is not difficult since they are less migratory as a group than many other birds. Holes where they have nested show clearly in trees bare of leaves, so a winter hike can locate several possible nest sites. Should any hole be low enough for examination with a ladder a second trip can be made with a lightweight set of kitchen steps or a section of aluminum ladder to permit each child to explore the inside of the hole.

In winter, also, birdfeeders can be placed where the children can watch them from a class meeting place. Woodpeckers, as well as other birds commonly about in winter and easy to identify when no leaves are on the trees, will welcome food at this time of year and come closer to a window to get it than they would be willing to come during the season when food is more plentiful. A word of warning: do not start to feed birds in the winter unless you plan to keep it up until natural food is again available, or more birds may stay in the area than the area can care for.

In case it should be necessary to give the children a second-hand experience through the use of pictures, films, slides, or tapes and records of bird calls, it will still be possible to do something which in some parts of the country may give them a personal acquaintance with a flicker family the following summer. This can be done by allowing each child to make a wooden nest box to place on his own home property before the spring nesting season comes.

Flickers want a good deep nest box, one 18 to 24 inches deep and 8 inches in diameter, with a 2½-inch hole at least 15 inches from the bottom on one side. Some chips and sawdust should be left inside to keep the eggs from rolling around, or the flicker will have to provide these by hammering chips loose from the box. It may be necessary for the children to have help with these boxes, in which case the teacher might mimeograph the instructions and send them home with the children as a suggestion for a father-child activity that will further the work of the course. Flicker nest boxes should be placed high enough on posts or trees to safeguard the baby birds from cats or dogs.

In the story to be read later, some Christmas surprises are described, and these can be made at work parties before Christmas to be used as gifts related to what the children have been doing: suet-covered pine cones, sunflower seeds and strings of cranberries and popcorn which will attract other birds which are not meat eaters. Even a city fire escape has sparrows and pigeons who would enjoy a Christmas feast.

As with the robin study, adults soon discover that children

as young as five and six will have more interest in the birds that come down to feed near their eye level than in the ones which are hard to locate high in the trees above them.

Certainly if the life cycle of birds was not discussed in connection with the robin study the teacher will want to introduce this in connection with the woodpecker, for the life story of any bird is of perennial interest to children.

OTHER POSSIBLE EXPERIENCES WITH WOODPECKERS

1. In Blough's *Making and Using Classroom Science Materials* (on page 70), there are a number of pictures, along with instructions for making a variety of simple bird-feeding stations. For younger children this will be a more satisfying experience than making nesting boxes to be used during the following summer. Some of these are so simple that they can be easily finished in a single class session, and all children can find a window where this sort of bird watching can be done. This may lead into an interest in other kinds of birds, but its most likely result will be an interest in birds in general. The recognition of a wide variety of species cannot be expected until children are older, unless of course they develop a spontaneous interest in the subject, as an occasional child does.

2. The "tap tap" of the woodpecker could lead into rhythmic play with drums. If the sound has been heard on a trip, or if a trip can be made to hear it, the children can try to catch the rhythm of the woodpecker on drums. Then they might like to try sounding out the rhythm of the syllables in their own names, or perhaps each of them would like to make up a rhythm of his own and see if the other children can learn to recognize it From such simple rhythm experiences the more complicated forms of the dance will grow.

3. Since by now the group has had experience with sand, the tree, robins, cats, and woodpeckers it would be a good time to start a large cooperative mural of the sandbox, the tree, and the living things thus far found around it. This should be made a

continuing project of the class if it is started, and the children should feel free to add items not discussed in class if they so desire.

4. If the birds' songs were used with the robin experience they might be extended to this new bird, and a song could be written. This is another chance to bring in taped or recorded bird calls. Some children may learn to recognize a few of them.

5. The children can make the feeding logs which will later be described to them when they hear the story of "The Tree Policeman" at the end of this experience. These can be taken home and used to attract birds.

6. As further preparation for the summarizing story, "The Tree Policeman," the group should go out to a tree and search in the bark to see if they can find more "meat for birds" than Alan and his mother are going to find in the story. Perhaps they will find *almost* as many as the woodpecker if the whole group looks carefully!

BOOKS FOR THE CHILDREN'S USE

We have found no books that deal specifically with the woodpecker. However if the leader will turn back to the list of books about birds in general which is given in connection with the "Experience with Robins" there will be more than adequate material to use in developing this experience with the woodpecker.

SONGS AND POEMS TO USE

Since the three sources we are using seem to have no poetry or songs about woodpeckers it might be suggested to the children that they make a book about woodpeckers for which they will write songs and poems themselves. If this is done the children could be allowed to draw their own illustrations on "ditto stencils" so that when they are finished the whole can be run off on the machine and each child may take home his own copy of the "special book we have made."

THE TREE POLICEMAN

NOT EVERY CREATURE that found food in the cherry tree above the sandbox lived in the children's own backyard. Nearly every day a red, black, and white bird flew out of a hole in a telephone pole at the corner of the block and spent some time on the trunk of the tree hunting for its favorite meat. This was the woodpecker.

The woodpecker's nest was a pile of wood chips inside a hole near the top of the pole. He and his mate had a family to feed. They had to visit many trees to find food for the babies while they were growing.

Alan, who played most often in the sandbox, noticed the woodpecker first one day in the early spring. He saw a bird hammering on the telephone pole with his long sharp beak, the red feathers on his head shining as he pounded. He seemed to be making a small hole bigger. The hammering was fast and loud.

"That bird better not make a hole in this tree," thought Alan. He was very fond of the cherry tree.

One day many weeks later he heard the cheerful, noisy call of a woodpecker as it flew toward the cherry tree. It made a quiet landing on the trunk about halfway up the tree and began poking at the bark. Alan could see that this bird had no red feathers on its head, so he guessed it was the mother bird. All the Terry children had learned that father birds usually have brighter colors than the mothers, who must sit on the nest.

The mother woodpecker was propping herself with her stiff tail and holding onto the bark with four sharp claws, two in front and two in the back of each foot. She poked a bit and then hopped to another place and poked some more.

Suddenly she flew away, straight back to the telephone pole. Alan thought she was carrying something in her beak, but he wasn't sure. Soon she was back again, doing the same thing. A small piece of bark fell right into Alan's upturned face.

Maybe this wasn't good for the tree. Alan ran into the house to find his mother.

"Is it all right for our cherry tree if that old woodpecker pecks around and knocks off pieces of bark?" he asked.

"It certainly is," said his mother. "He doesn't know it, but he's a sort of tree policeman protecting the trees where he hunts for food. Woodpeckers find bugs and grubs that might chew the wood of the tree and harm it. Right now I think they have to work harder than ever because they probably have babies to feed."

"Do we have gugs and brubs . . . I mean bugs and grubs in our cherry tree?"

Alan's mother laughed. "Let's go see if we can find any."

They peeled some bark away from a crack in the tree and found a tiny white cocoon. They saw an ant crawling on the tree, and Mrs. Terry said the woodpeckers would probably like to eat the ant as well as whatever was inside the cocoon. This was all they found that they thought might be meat for a bird.

"But the woodpecker is better at finding food inside the tree than we are," Alan's mother explained. "He has a long tongue with a hook on the end of it. He can feel around with the tip of his tongue inside the bark and pull out bugs and grubs, even out of holes wood-boring insects make in the wood to lay their eggs in."

"Well, I guess it's all right then," said Alan. "I was afraid he was hurting the tree instead of helping it. But I hope he doesn't ever dig a hole in it big enough for a nest."

"Woodpeckers seem to like trees without branches for their nests, and dead wood may be easier to dig into. Perhaps that's why they often make a nest in a telephone pole."

Alan looked down the block toward the telephone pole and wondered what kind of a tree it had been when it was alive. He had never thought of his cherry tree as "live wood" and the telephone pole as part of what had once been a living tree.

There were woodpeckers around the neighborhood all winter, but Alan couldn't tell whether they were the same ones, or some that had come from farther north where the cold was sure to last longer than it would here.

They seemed to be able to find enough insects hiding in the bark of trees to keep from getting too hungry, and he supposed there were empty holes to keep them warm at night and during storms. They ate berries from a vine on the side of a church nearby, and enjoyed food that people put out on their birdfeeders during the snowy weather.

At Christmas time the Terry family hung surprises on the cherry tree for the woodpeckers, the chickadees, and other winter birds. Mr. Terry saved some small logs (about 3 inches across) and sawed them into short lengths. He drilled several holes in each one, 1¼ inches wide and 1½ inches deep. Into these holes the children stuffed pieces of suet. Tom drove two long nails into opposite sides of the top end of each log, and Ann and Alan fastened wire to the nails so they could hang the logs over the branches. The birds had a wonderful time eating the kind of food they needed most to keep warm and strong in cold weather. And the children had fun refilling the logs when the birds had finished all the food.

When spring came again Alan's woodpecker came back to the same telephone pole and found a piece of tin on which to hammer early every morning.

"He's telling the other woodpeckers to stay away because he and his mate are going to use the same pole for their nest this year," Tom explained.

"O.K.," said Alan, even though he felt cross because the drumming had wakened him so early. "The cherry tree needs some tree policemen. It's a good thing he like to eat bugs. That's all they're good for, I guess."

But Alan and Ann and Tom discovered some very interesting bugs that spring, and they even brought them into the house!

INTRODUCTION TO THE EXPERIENCE TO FOLLOW

After the story about woodpeckers and bark beetles during the study of trees, and after hearing the "Tree Policeman" story, the children will probably begin to react as Alan does in the story when he belittles the usefulness of insects in the final paragraph of the story. This becomes the point to challenge them.

"Are bugs good for anything except as food for birds?"

"What *is* a bug? The same as an insect?"

"Are there any insects that help to keep living things in balance the same way the woodpecker does?" "What about the spider?"

"Would you like to see how many kinds of spiders we can find in a half hour? We will need to have those jars again for the next session!"

EXPERIENCE WITH

Spiders

DEVELOPING THE EXPERIENCE

AFTER THOUSANDS OF YEARS of coexistence it would seem that we might know by now that spiders are essential to our welfare. But the myths and fears passed from one generation to another live on, and few indeed are those who pass along the scientific truth that there are only two spiders in our country (and not many in the world) capable of seriously harming a human. One American authority, H. C. McCook, doubts if man could survive without the large numbers of spiders that live around us.

It is time we began listening to the people who really know about spiders and realize that almost all living creatures might starve if it weren't for the great numbers of insect-eating spiders over the earth. An English naturalist, John Crompton, has estimated that in England and Wales twenty-two trillion "harmful" insects are eaten by spiders in one year!

Even the black widow, one of our native spiders with a sometimes fatal poison in its bite, deserves credit as well as respectful treatment, for it serves mankind by supplying silk for delicate instruments, as well as by killing quantities of insects that multiply rapidly. The black widow spider is recognized by the red marks on the abdomen. The brown house spider, easily identified, is the other harmful spider. However, many scientists

57

blame the few deaths that have occurred from spider bite on allergy, infection, or heart condition. Spider bite is usually not at all serious, and it is easily avoidable. The methods of study suggested here should be sufficient to avoid any danger.

No one has to go far afield to study spiders. With an illustrated book for identifying specimens, a number of glass jars with gauze-covered cotton balls as stoppers, a stick for gently dislodging spiders and guiding them into the jar, and a magnifying glass, anyone can soon find and carry home several varieties for identification and study. There must be a separate jar for each captive. Spider-watching in classroom or field is fascinating for both children and adults.

Most spiders are beautiful. Bright colors, stripes, spots, and mottling decorate them. Those that spin webs delight and amaze us with their skill, and it is quite possible that wherever a teacher and a group of children are sitting they may find a spider web close by. If it is a circular net somewhat like a wheel of gossamer lace, it is called an orb web. An orb web with zigzag "writing" on it is the web of a garden spider. But there are other orb webs woven by other types of spider.

In addition to the orb there are three contrasting types of web, the irregular mesh of the house spider, the funnel web of the grass spider, and the sheet web of the common "bowl and doily" spider. Other kinds of spiders make other varieties of orb, irregular mesh, funnel, or sheet webs, too.

Then there are the spiders who use no web for catching their prey. The bold wolf spiders, the delicate green lynx, the runners, and the jumpers are among them. They may use web silk to make their nests or nurseries, their trap-door hinges or their egg cases, but they *hunt* insects instead of catching them in nets.

In spite of the early example of Miss Muffet, once exposed to the true nature of these small, shy creatures, children are easily converted to a scientific attitude toward spiders. They recognize our debt to the gifted weavers and become conscious of them everywhere, seeking opportunities to observe them just as we do birds, butterflies, and moths. And they can share in the horror of scientists who watch ignorant insect-fighters wipe out with poison sprays the birds and spiders who keep down the insect population.

Stories abound to enrich classroom study of spiders. A Greek legend about the goddess Arachne is the source of the scientific name of the spider class. American Indian legends about the spider are plentiful. The tale of Robert Bruce, inspired to continue a fight for his country's freedom by the persistence of a small spider, has as much impact upon children today as when it was first told.

There is a great drama in the daily life of spiders. They have many enemies, many problems to solve in order to find their food and raise their families.

A "bring-them-back-alive" expedition to capture spiders for the opening of a temporary spider zoo requires some preparation. Before it is undertaken each child in the group should have some idea of where to look for the various kinds of spider to be expected in the locality. By the use of pictures and stories about each one (the stories easily abridged in simple words from the information given with the picture), the books in the classroom provide all that children need to know in order to make the expedition interesting. There is no cruelty involved in the captivity of spiders for they can go without food for long periods of time.

Since our aim is helping children to learn respect for life while they are studying it, rather than teaching them how to be professional zoo keepers or zoologists, it is better not to allow them to feed live insects to captive spiders. It is quite possible that before many weeks the children may be studying the very insect that forms part of the spider's diet, and with the same interest and respect akin to reverence that they feel toward their spider captive today. It is enough at this age for them to know what insects the spider eats, or they can observe the spider eating in a natural outdoor situation.

A general rule may be adopted to this effect: "Use no living creature for food for other creatures in captivity. Instead, release the captives soon and observe their feeding habits in the field." This demonstrates an attitude of "hands off unless absolutely necessary" familiar to conservationists.

Winter in cold climates finds some outdoor spiders still in unhatched eggs, some as hatched infants still within the egg, some as juveniles in a cocoon, and others as adults wintering under dry leaves, in beds of dry mosses, hidden by stones or tree bark, and often wrapped in layers of their own silk. It should be possible to find a number of varieties indoors at any time of year.

Spider web collections, although more difficult to achieve than a spider zoo, are quite possible. The following instructions for collecting webs are taken from *The Web Weavers* (Boston, Beacon Press, 1964). Similar instructions can also be found in *The Golden Book of Nature Activities* previously listed in one of our bibliographies.

> It is possible to collect webs if you are patient, and work very carefully. First find a web, then take some dark construction paper or cardboard large enough to cover the whole web. You will also need some white spray paint. Use this carefully, noticing which way the wind is blowing, so no one will get in the way of the paint. Be sure that there is nothing behind the web that the paint would harm. Spray the web carefully from a distance. Now place the paper back of the web without disturbing the web. Be sure that every strand of silk is touching the paper. Snip off any web around the edges and capture the web from its surroundings. There you will have the spider's work outlined for you in all its beauty on your sheet of paper. The wet paint will act as glue. When it is dry you may want to spray it with a plastic spray to preserve it, or cover it with Saran wrap.

With these children of younger ages than *The Web Weavers* was written for, the leader will need to assist with the process, but the children can find the specimens and can do much of the work with only a little adult guidance. The collections are interesting when completed, and some of the webs are truly beautiful.

Children enjoy watching spider acrobatics in the classroom. This is easily arranged by placing a spider high in the room so he can drop a line of silk, climb back up the same strand, or swing on it to attach it somewhere else and start weaving a web. Whatever he does provides pleasure and surprise.

In between collecting, observing, and identifying, the children may need games and songs like "Itsy, Bitsy, Spider," and finally the story summarizing this experience, "The Great Spider Zoo," can bring their experience into focus as a part of the picture of interdependent life in a backyard.

OTHER POSSIBLE EXPERIENCES WITH SPIDERS

1. Watching the weaving of a web gives an excellent opportunity for making first a story, then a dance of the web weavers. In the *Golden Book of Nature Activities* is a diagram showing the order in which web weaving for the orb web is done. Using sticks stuck in the sand, or chairs, let the children dramatize the spider's routine (and don't forget to "jerk" the strand each time). They may also want to dramatize the spider and the insects he catches. "Won't you come into my parlor?" might start this activity. After the web weaving and the story have been dramatized, they may well telescope into a single dance.

2. Older children may want to use a pencil or crayon instead of physical activity to diagram the making of the orb web. (Or trying to make one with nylon fishing cord or silk thread will certainly show how difficult the process is — for them!)

3. After the story has been read, or perhaps as a spontaneous suggestion from the children beforehand, the group may want to have its own "Great Spider Zoo" and invite some other class in to view the collection of spiders, webs, and drawings, and to share the dance the class has created.

4. Because the children will probably not have had much past experience with spiders they may be interested in making their own "spider books," with pictures of the various spiders they have found and drawings of the type of web they have seen. If real webs were collected they might be used as the covers for these booklets.

BOOKS FOR THE CHILDREN'S USE

Children's Books About Spiders

> Adrian, Mary. *Garden Spider*. Holiday House.
> Life cycle of miranda. Simple easy reading, but a great

deal of information and written with charm.

Cooke, D. Irma. *The Web Weavers*. Beacon Press.

This unit in the Beacon Science Series though for slightly older children contains much material on the spider myths, and also some excellent and evocative photographs.

David, Eugene. *Spiders and How They Live*. Prentice-Hall.

A "Junior Research Book," which starts the children on a search for more information and urges them to do their own observation. Much information also.

Goldin, Augusta. *Spider Silk*. Crowell.

Simpler and less inclusive than Shuttleworth, but the charm of the illustrations, and the easy reading level, make this book a real addition to the classroom library.

Hogner, Dorothy Childs. *Spiders*. Crowell.

A useful reference, complete and well written, though not as colorful as Shuttleworth.

Lougee, Laura Barr. *The Web of the Spider*. Cranbrook Institute of Science.

Lovely pictures of the spider's web. Not as much information as is contained in most of the other books on the list, but worth having, if possible, for the pictures.

Shuttleworth, Dorothy. *The Story of Spiders*. Doubleday.

Large, clear, colorful illustrations which are sure to arouse interest; detailed information to satisfy the interest aroused. This book is one of the best of the spider books.

Adult Book About Spiders

Crompton, John. *The Life of the Spider*. New American Library.

This Mentor Paperback (M 105) will go along with the children's material, and its wealth of material for the adult to share will help many adults develop their own interest in these creatures.

SONGS AND POEMS TO USE

"Spiders": page 89 in *Poems To Grow On*.

"Spider Webs": page 93 in *Poems To Grow On.*
"See What Is Here!": Number 33 in *Martin and Judy Songs.*

STORY TO SUMMARIZE THE EXPERIENCE

"THE GREAT SPIDER ZOO"

TOM, ANN, AND ALAN were given a tent one fall by a neighbor who was moving away. His own children were grown and he had no further use for the tent, but the Terry children certainly did! They set it up near the cherry tree in the backyard and played in it even on rainy days. One very warm evening they asked their parents if they could sleep in the tent, and after that they spent many nights in three sleeping bags which fitted nicely under the sloping shelter of the canvas.

Mr. and Mrs. Terry had warned the children to be quiet if they woke up early in the morning so as not to bother the sleeping neighbors. So when Alan was wakened by a mosquito one morning, he stayed in his sleeping bag without making any noise. He tried to catch the mosquito humming above his face, but it dodged away from his hand every time he tried to reach it. And then *it was caught,* but not by Alan. Near the top of the tent was a spider web, and the mosquito became entangled in its lowest threads.

The web was large and round. It made Alan think of a wheel. The first rays of sunlight were coming through the tent flaps and shining on the web so he could see it plainly. A black spider with pretty yellow markings sat in the center of the wheel. When the mosquito became tangled in a silky strand of the outer rim, the spider seemed to feel a quiver of one of the threads. Anyway it ran quickly to the mosquito and began to wrap it in more and more silk until it looked like a tiny cocoon. Alan saw where the silk came from: just where the spider's tail would have been if it had a tail.

Alan's cheek was beginning to itch where the mosquito had bitten him before he woke up.

"It got its breakfast from me," thought Alan, "and now the spider is probably going to have it for breakfast." Sure enough, the spider was dragging her tiny package of mosquito meat to the center of the web as though she intended to have it for breakfast. Just then Alan heard his mother making coffee in the kitchen, so he slipped out of his sleeping bag, stepped carefully over the one in which Ann was sleeping, and scampered into the house to have his own breakfast.

No one else was awake. Alan and his mother ate together at the kitchen table. He told her about the mosquito and the spider.

"I didn't think I liked spiders, but I was certainly glad she got that old mosquito. You should have seen the way she wrapped it up. I'd like to see how spiders make those webs."

"After Tom and Ann are out of the tent let's move your spider to a place where we can watch her spin a new web," suggested Mrs. Terry. "Then she can catch more mosquitoes, flies, and other insects. Spiders are a great help around the yard. If spiders and birds didn't eat the insects that fly, there would soon be so many of them swarming around that we might not have any garden at all. You know insects are apt to be leaf nibblers."

"Mosquitoes are people nibblers," said Alan, touching the itching red spot on his cheek.

Later they moved the garden spider to a bush beside the back porch, and all morning they watched her making another perfect wheel-shaped web. This was so interesting they began to look for other spiders. Tom got his bicycle out and rode to the library for a book with colored pictures of many different kinds of spiders so they could learn about others. With several of their friends, he and Ann and Alan spent that whole day searching the backyard, the porches, and a nearby vacant lot to see how many different kinds of spiders they could find.

They carried glass jars with cotton balls stuffed in the top. The book suggested this instead of jar lids with holes because some of the spiders might be small enough to crawl out through an air hole. They were careful not to put more than one spider into each jar. When they had six jars on the floor of the Terrys' back porch they examined their specimens and looked them up in the book to see what kinds of spiders they had found.

There were three garden spiders, one wolf spider, two little grass spiders, a crab spider, and a daddy longlegs. Then Mrs.

Terry came out with a house spider, and they had six different kinds in their collection.

It was Tom who thought of having a spider zoo.

"This book says spiders live for days without eating, so we won't be cruel if we keep them for a while. We can sell tickets for five cents and have everyone come at the same time. Each of us can be in charge of a different jar and we can tell the people about our spiders."

Mrs. Terry liked the idea and said she would help by typing labels to go on the jars giving the right name for each spider. They decided to open the zoo on Friday evening at seven o'clock.

The tent was a good place to have the zoo. Soon there was a sign across the front of the tent saying "GREAT SPIDER ZOO. Admission 5 cents." Ann went to every house on the block selling tickets.

On Friday night one of Alan's friends sat at a table made from a box, just outside the tent, and took the tickets from all who came. The audience was invited to sit on the grass in front of the open tent. Just inside was a long board standing on two boxes. The six glass jars stood on this board, each with a boy or girl standing behind it.

At seven o'clock Tom stepped forward with his jar and stood in front of the audience.

"I have in here a wolf spider. It lives in a nest and goes after insects like a hunter. The only web it spins is to make its nest soft and the mother makes a sac to carry her eggs in until they hatch. But they don't catch their food in webs. They have hair on them almost like fur. They stay hidden in their nests all winter. Mine is a pretty brown one."

Tom then passed his jar and a magnifying glass all around the audience. Everyone had a chance to see the wolf spider.

"I have a garden spider," said Ann. "They catch insects in their webs. This protects us from too many insects. The webs are beautiful, big, and round. My garden spider has orange marks on its body, and I like it."

After everyone had looked at the garden spider it was Alan's turn.

"This is a little crab spider," he said. "It's shaped like a crab. It's sitting on a yellow flower and it looks rather yellow. When I found it, it was white. It can change back to white if I put it on a white flower. Crab spiders run sideways like crabs do. They don't spin webs to catch their food. They eat little insects that might eat your flowers."

The other children did just as well as the three Terrys.

After the spiders had all been shown Mrs. Terry served lemonade to everyone. Then she read something from the spider book that said people might starve to death and all other living creatures too, if there weren't so many spiders everywhere protecting fields and gardens.

"But aren't some spiders dangerous?" a neighbor asked.

Tom was expecting this question. He read a part of the book that said spiders don't like to bite people, and if they ever do it's not a serious bite except for two spiders in our country: the black widow spider and the brown house spider. "These two spiders are easy to recognize and avoid," Tom went on. "Spiders are shy. They try to get away from people. You can be a good spider watcher without touching them."

All the people in the audience learned a lot about spiders and decided to watch them at home. The Great Spider Zoo was a real success.

INTRODUCTION TO THE EXPERIENCE TO FOLLOW

In preparing for an experience with a mole or shrew, use can be made of the comments in the spider story about the rapid reproduction of insects, and what the world would be like if insects were not used as food by so many other forms of life. The children should remember that the woodpecker protected the tree from insect damage. Swallows may have been swooping about catching insects on the wing during some of the outdoor explorations of the group, so the children may be aware by now that many kinds of birds catch flying insects. And by now they have discovered the role spiders play in the backyard, keeping in balance the numbers of insects and the numbers of plants and animals they need to live on. But what about the insects on the ground and in it? The leader will want to give the children time to try to answer this question. Then the leader might ask: would the children like to be detectives and find out whether there are ground or grass "policemen" hunting insects under the ground and in the grass?

What kind of creature does this?

What animals live in the ground?

Which ones eat insects?

Moles
and Shrews

DEVELOPING THE EXPERIENCE

THE STORY which is to follow this adventure study deals specifically with shrews rather than moles because shrews are to be found even in the desert and high mountains, whereas moles are not. However, because it is so difficult to see shrews alive, if there are moles to be found in the area a group experience with them may be easier to plan and arrange. These mammals will be found on adjacent pages in reference books, so if the children look up pictures of either one they are likely to find the other. Having seen pictures of both animals, when the children hear the story "The Unseen Hunter" it will not be about a creature strange to them even though their actual experience may have been with moles.

Since a number of varieties of mice live in holes abandoned by moles it is quite possible that these lively creatures, which are already familiar to most children, will also come into the discussion and perhaps into the experience.

Like spiders, moles are much maligned by the average person. Gardeners are too busy thinking of ways to get rid of moles to spend time learning what the moles are doing down there under the lawn. When ridges appear on the grassy surface after a rain, accompanied by piles of dirt, moles are eating insects that

68

destroy plant roots which may compensate for the temporary damage they have done to the appearance of the lawn. And in the course of their hunting they aerate the soil by loosening it, a further compensation.

If the first clue in the search for "ground policemen" is sought in a book on small mammals, moles will soon be discovered. The leader should have already learned what kind of moles are to be found in the area: the eastern mole, the fantastic star-nosed mole, the California, Pacific, or shrew mole. And what is it likely to be doing at this time of year?

Moles do not hibernate. They hunt for food all winter and have their families of two to five babies in tunnel nests early in the spring. Star-nosed moles are swimmers, and their tunnels often lead into a stream where they find food on the bottom of the water. Open pasture land and fields where the soil is loose, as well as well-kept grassy areas, are the preferred locale for moles. If the leader does some advance scouting or consults with local biology experts, it should be possible to take the children to a place where moles, or at least their tunnels, can be found. Some people use harmless traps for moles, and then take them into the woods away from the lawn they are trying to protect. The biologist may know someone who does this, and it might be possible to thus find a live mole for the class session. Or some father may be willing to trap one or two from his lawn. A description of building such a trap is found in *A Field Book of Nature Activities* by William Hillcourt (G. P. Putnam's Sons), as well as in many other nature books.

Some towns and cities have museums where stuffed mammals are displayed. If a mole is among them, permission may be secured for the children to handle and examine the specimen. Because there is nothing threatening or frightening about a soft little mole which can't see very well, even in daylight, children can enjoy them and like to hear stories about them. *Freddy the Cat* by Grace Paull has a mole as the center of interest, and delights young children. And for a touch of fantasy to season reality the older ones can enjoy the home reading of Kenneth Grahame's *Wind in the Willows* while they are studying about real moles. Even young children will delight in the story of Mole's house, or the episode where the little field mice come to sing Christmas carols to him.

Young children can have fun playing "mole in a tunnel." A tunnel is made with tables or chairs and those who wish to play are blindfolded. The others are judges. The "moles" in turn crawl through the tunnel as quietly as they can, pretending to dig their way with two out-turned paws. Those who are judging close their eyes and concentrate on listening for sounds from the tunnel. When they hear a sound they put up a hand and the teacher counts the number of times hands are raised during each mole's trip through the tunnel. Those making the least sound are the best moles.

Moles and shrews can be reproduced in clay, in plush-textured cloth, in collages of cloth on paper, or in drawing and painting. Their shape is simple and easy for a child to reproduce. Tunnels can be made from paper tubes fastened together for toy moles to be pulled through with a string. Since this is an experience where the direct contact with the living creature will be limited and difficult to achieve, some vicarious experience may well have to be offered.

The expression "making a mountain out of a molehill" will have more meaning to children who have examined a molehill; and they will enjoy hearing that the name of "shrew" has been used to describe cross, scolding, angry women with shrill voices because shrews make such a noise when fighting over food.

The amount of actual observation of moles or shrews will depend upon the ingenuity and resourcefulness of the adult leader, the locale, and the season of the year; but it is possible with this subject to substitute replicas for the living creature if it is impossible to find a live mole or shrew.

OTHER POSSIBLE EXPERIENCES WITH THE MOLE AND SHREW

1. The story suggests how the children played the game of guessing what was a mammal or a bird. A simple variation of the old familiar game "bird, beast, or fish?" could be played with the words bird–insect–mammal to help children become familiar

with these technical names. Even quite small children enjoy knowing the "real names" of things.

2. Since moles are nearly blind the children could put blindfolds on and see how well they can make their way around the room, find the table where their "insects" (juice and crackers) are, and so forth. This would be simpler in a crowded classroom than the "mole in a tunnel" game, or might be added to it.

3. This is an experience that needs to be given depth by the use of as many pictures as can be found, since these animals are not easily observed.

4. One interesting experience, although it is indirect, is to go to a place where moles are active in the lawn, and find a spot where the mole is working. If the children sit very quietly the mole will continue his digging, and it is fascinating to watch the earth heave up ahead of him and to follow his pattern across the lawn. He *might* even come to the surface, although this is not likely. Children will also enjoy following the tunnels across the lawn, seeing how far the mole has gone and tracing his journey. This is an activity that is possible wherever a lawn has been used by the moles.

5. The group can go food hunting, again with their jars, and catch as many of the insects mentioned in the story as they can. The teacher can help them weigh their "catch" before it is released (by weighing the jar ahead of time and then reweighing it after the hunt) and see how much "shrew" dinner they have collected. Did the total catch of the class equal the weight of even one shrew? Perhaps this experience will help the children to realize a little more clearly the constant hunt necessary for these tiny creatures in their fight against hunger.

BOOKS FOR THE CHILDREN'S USE

Children's Books About Moles, Shrews, and Mice

Kane, Henry B. *The Tale of the Whitefoot Mouse.* Knopf.
Beautiful photographs and poetic prose make the reading of this book a valuable experience in itself. It

starts when the family is less than a day old and follows
their development and life.

Peterson, Barbara and Russell. *Whitefoot Mouse.* Holiday House.

More detailed than the Kane book. This has drawings
instead of photographs. The two books supplement each
other nicely and should both be available.

Ripper, Charles L. *Moles and Shrews.* Morrow.

This contains clear drawings, and many diagrams, with
much detail not elsewhere available. A wide variety of
moles and shrews are considered.

SONGS AND POEMS TO USE

"The House of the Mouse": page 103 in *Poems To Grow On.*

STORY TO SUMMARIZE THE EXPERIENCE

THE UNSEEN HUNTER

IT WAS BECAUSE OF Mrs. Cat and her habit of hunting at night
that the Terry children learned about a remarkable little animal living in their backyard without their knowing it. One
morning when Mr. Terry left the house to go to work he stopped
to pick up something from the driveway, and then came back to
show the family what he had found.

In his hand was a little brownish animal covered with soft
fur. It was dead. At first Alan thought it was the body of a small
mouse, but then he noticed that it had a long pointed nose and
very tiny ears and eyes. It was more like the moles the cat sometimes caught, except that this little animal had feet like a mouse
instead of large-toed feet for digging like the mole.

"It's a shrew," said Mr. Terry, "the body of a dead shrew."
He stroked the soft fur with the tip of his finger. "Mrs. Cat must
have caught it last night."

"Why didn't she eat it?" asked Alan.

"I've heard that shrews give out an odor to drive their
enemies away, so cats aren't apt to eat them. I guess they don't
taste good to the cat."

"But why did it die, then?" Tom wondered out loud. "There's no mark on its fur to show it was hurt."

"I think I know," said Mrs. Terry. "When I was a little girl your grandpa told me that shrews have to eat nearly every minute of their lives, and Mrs. Cat probably played with this one and chased it so long that it wasn't able to eat soon enough. They have to eat as much food in one day as they weigh. What if you had to eat a pile of food as heavy as you are in one day, and hunt for it too?"

"But why do they have to eat so much?" asked Ann.

Tom had learned the answer to this question at school. "They're so little and so very active they can't store up enough energy to last them very long. They move so quickly we seldom see them and they fight fiercely for their food if another creature tries to take it from them. Everything they do is done fast and furiously. They use up all the energy they can get from what they eat in just a few minutes, and then they have to eat again. We don't use up our energy from food as fast as that."

Mrs. Terry agreed. "We can get along for about four hours without getting hungry because we're big enough to store up the energy from a good meal. At night we go for many hours without eating because sleeping doesn't use up as much energy as working and playing. And it takes quite a few days for a man to starve to death. But look at this little shrew. How tiny its stomach must be!" Mrs. Terry touched the soft bit of fur.

Mr. Terry really had to start for work now, so he picked up the shrew and put it on a piece of paper on the kitchen table. "You can look at it some more," he said. "Then you will know a shrew if you should ever be quick enough to see one alive. But please bury it after you are through. Then it will give back to the soil some of what it has taken from the soil in order to live."

"I don't know what he means," said Ann after her father had gone.

"Think about it and see if you can figure it out," suggested Mrs. Terry, who had some work to do then.

After their mother left the room, Alan and Ann and Tom stood around the table where the shrew's little body lay.

"I guess he means the shrews get food from the soil. I wonder what they eat. I wonder if they make tunnels like moles."

Tom picked up the little shrew and looked at its feet, then he showed them to Ann and Alan. "What do you think?" he asked.

Alan thought of an answer first. "Moles have feet for digging. These feet wouldn't be very good for that. But perhaps he runs in the mole's tunnels the way mice sometimes do, hunting for food. Let's find out."

First the children looked in the dictionary, but that didn't tell them any more than they already knew. Tom asked his mother if he could ride to the library on his bicycle and get a book about moles and shrews. She said he certainly could.

"Ask for a book about small mammals," she suggested. "All the animals, big and little, that can grow hair and give milk to their babies and have a bony frame inside instead of a shell or no bones at all are called mammals. There are so many of them, it's likely the small mammals will be in a separate book."

Ann heard her mother explain this to Tom. After he was gone she hurried back to the kitchen to tell Alan.

While they waited for Tom to come back they had fun thinking of all the animals they could that were mammals. Sometimes they made mistakes and laughed at each other.

"Not birds, silly. They do have bones inside, but they have feathers instead of hair, and they don't give milk to their babies."

"How about fish? No, not fish!"

"Well, how about us? Yes, people must be mammals. Mother," Ann called, "Mother, are we mammals?"

When Tom came back from the library Ann and Alan told him that people are related to shrews because they are both mammals. He was surprised that they knew this.

Mrs. Terry joined the children and helped them read the story about shrews in the library book. They learned that shrews burrow into rotted leaves or loose topsoil, under a rock or a log or stump where they can make nests of leaves or grass. But they learned that they find their food on top of the ground: insects, grubs, worms, centipedes, and snails, even young mice and some nuts or berries.

"Well, shrews do get their food from the soil, because all those things come out of the ground or live right on it," said Tom.

"And what they eat turns into fur and bones and all the parts of a live, growing shrew," added his mother. "If they are buried when they are no longer living, these rich chemicals go back into the soil again as your father said. Then new life can use it, plants or creatures that eat plants."

Alan found this hard to understand, but he did remember that his father had asked them to bury the shrew. He reminded the others. So they put the tiny body into a hole in the garden and covered it with earth.

Alan and Ann went off to play, but Tom spent a long time looking for a live shrew in the yard. The book said these tiny creatures run so fast through the grass and dead leaves that it is very hard to see them. Once Tom saw something moving under some leaves and hurried to look, but he found only a slow worm-like creature with many legs. He had seen these before and knew it was a millipede.

"Better watch out," he told it softly," or a shrew will get you for one of its all-day dinners."

That night the children told their father what they had learned about shrews and where they had buried the one Mrs. Cat had caught. They never did manage to see a live shrew in their yard, but now they knew that while the woodpecker was catching insects on the trees, and spiders were catching insects that flew in the air or that crawled on flowers, moles and shrews were catching the ones that lived on the ground and in it. Not all of them, of course, but enough insects so that there were never too many.

Alan called the woodpeckers "tree policemen," and he called the spiders, moles, and shrews "garden policemen" or "grass policemen."

The grass seemed to be full of things that were alive and busy. If he watched even one small part of it, he could count a surprising number of creatures that seemed to need it.

As he explored the grass, he learned that insects were useful to the backyard too, and not just as food for the insect-eaters!

INTRODUCTION TO THE EXPERIENCE TO FOLLOW

After this story is read the children will again tie their discoveries about an appealing little animal into the interdependent backyard community of people, plants, and creatures. They
can add "moles and shrews need insects, too; and insects need
the mole and shrew" to their "needing song."

It is quite likely that the story telling about burying the
mole may bring up questions about burying other pets, or about
burying people. The teacher should think through these things
in case the discussion arises. She may want to be prepared with
the stories about death which are in *The Tuckers* or in *The
Family Finds Out,* both books in the Beacon Series in Religious
Education (Beacon Press).

Surely in their search for a "shrew dinner" the children
will come upon ants, and the ants which crawl in the grass are
to be the subject of the next experience. The leader can wonder
out loud again:

"I wonder what ants eat?"

"If we watched some ants, we could find out. Where do
you suppose we could find a lot of ants to watch?"

"A book might tell us where they live. Next time we're
together we'll see what we can find. If you find any
ants near your homes watch them and see what you
can learn."

EXPERIENCE WITH

Ants

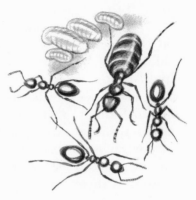

DEVELOPING THE EXPERIENCE

AFTER THE CHILDREN have had some experiences with insect-eating creatures, they may feel that the only real use for "bugs" is being food for other animals. It is high time they learned more about insects, and the approach of warmer weather will make it easier to observe insect life.

In the story "The Unseen Hunter," Alan has expressed some interest in exploring what goes on in the grass. Should the children like this idea the teacher can locate an ant nest between sessions of the group and lead them to the patch of grass (not necessarily a lawn) nearest to the ant colony. Discovery of the ants and tracing of their trails to the nest will follow.

By now it should be apparent to the children that variety exists in the world of creatures. They know that there are many kinds of birds, for instance. If no child wonders out loud what kind of ants these are, the teacher may certainly do so. As soon as a child's reference book on ants is consulted, the vast variety in the ant world will be opened to their curiosity.

Several such books describe ways of capturing ant colonies in homemade ant houses, and any method may be used that seems feasible to the teacher. (These may also be purchased commercially.) This is the ideal way to observe ant life fully. The colony can be kept for a long time if it is properly cared for, and if the children make their own ant house they may wish to pass it on as a gift to another group of children when they have enjoyed it thoroughly.

If the ant house means of study is not used, and it is necessary to observe the colony in its natural surroundings, younger children will soon tire of watching because the amount of activity that can be seen from above the ground is limited. But the story of life within the colony can be read aloud and then individual ants brought into the classroom for observation and later returned to their home. Inch-high walls of plaster of paris, in powder form, on the children's worktable will contain the ants which can be observed (preferably through magnifying glasses) as they clean themselves, greet each other, carry food, follow odor trails, overcome obstacles, and so forth. Ants are not difficult to draw, and the children may want to make a large group drawing of the activity which they have observed.

Ants live longer than most insects. They are easily the most successful and numerous of insects, and their role of scavenger is important in the refertilization of soil, for most of them bury organic material in their nests. They are to be found in every part of the country, but the varieties differ in different places. In the southwestern United States, for instance, the honey-pot ants provide a fascinating chapter in the story of adaptation. Harvester ants are also found in the southwest, their nests easily identifiable by the roads leading to the entrance.

Ants feel shadows, drink dewdrops, and carry water to moisten their nests. Ants keep their nests clean. They have rooms in their houses and move their babies about as they grow and as the dampness or warmth of the room changes. They may have summer and winter nests, choosing protected places under stumps and rocks for winter homes. Some varieties keep herds of aphids, using as food the honey dew they exude.

Ants have combs on their front legs and tongues for cleaning themselves. If they meet a friend they touch each other with their antennae, and they give food to their queens and their babies from the tip of their tongues. Children can observe much of this activity.

In the course of looking for ants in a reference book, the

boys and girls may become interested in termites, or some of the children may come from homes where termites are causing damage and be very much aware of them. Recently a biologist mother found a log in the woods being destroyed by termites. She took a large piece of the wood in a well-covered container for a group of nursery school children to see. They were able to hear the chewing going on within the wood, and also the threatening clicks made by the soldier termites when the wood was disturbed. This experience suggests that it should be possible to find wood in which either termites or carpenter ants are working and to cover the tunneled area with glass as the work of these amazing insects is watched. Housewreckers or exterminators in pest control firms could be a source of such a piece of wood from a home invaded by insects, and suggest ways of disposing of it when the observation is finished.

A wonderful way of learning about the lives of mushroom-growing ants or harvesters is by watching a sketch artist illustrate, while the story is told, each step of the activities described, using large drawings on a blackboard or a sheet of white paper on a wall. Even an "inartistic" teacher could soon learn to draw these simple but clear diagrams which would make the telling of the story more interesting.

During ant study the children may enjoy being organized in the manner of the ants when they are about to attempt something as a group. Certain duties could be assigned to workers of various kinds, so that they may better appreciate the degree of efficiency achieved by the "assignment" of work within an ant colony.

During a relaxed time, such as when they are lying on the grass together, an imaginative group can pretend to be ants and describe to each other what the grass looks like as they start to hunt for food, how large a dead bumblebee appears in front of them on their trail, and how they could carry it back to their nest. Adopting an "ant's-eye view" can be fun if not carried on too long.

An indoor game can help the children to identify with the trail-following problems of the ant. They will understand that their own sense of smell is not good enough to do what the ant does (although one might try a perfume trail on a linoleum floor), but they can try to follow a trail by feeling it with their bare feet. Blindfolded they can try to cross the room on a zigzag trail made of some material different from the floor and not wider than the width of their feet. If they lose the trail, they must wander until their feet find it again as the ant does in searching for an odor trail.

OTHER POSSIBLE EXPERIENCES WITH ANTS

1. Older children can draw the scene as seen by us, and as seen by the ant. Get eyes at ground level for perspective and discuss relative size of a blade of grass, a crumb, and so forth. Sometimes this sort of new perspective will give a quality to the child's drawing that is different, as well as teaching him simple lessons in careful observation.

2. If an ant house is not built, a clay model could be made from the various diagrams that will be found in the ant books, and little snips of black pipe cleaner could serve as the ants in the model. It will help the children visualize the ant home if they have a three-dimensional model, and it will help them remember because they have made it.

3. Although the rest of the sequence is much too difficult for children, there is one sonnet in Edna St. Vincent Millay's "Epitaph for the Race of Man" which is about a farmer and an ant who meet each other on the road, and do not realize that their problems are the same. It will be found in *Wine from These Grapes* or, of course, in her *Collected Works*. This will lend itself to discussion, to dramatics, or to picture making.

4. An interesting activity is discovering the number of insects which can be found in a limited space. For instance, digging up a cubic foot of earth and spreading it out, then seeing how many different things there are in it. The teacher who has not done this before may be as amazed as the children. Rich soil should be used, as this will contain more materials. Another possibility is to take part of an old rotten log, and pull this apart to see how

many creatures are living in it. The wealth of variety of creatures we can know and study is an important thing for children to discover.

5. The study of ants also will lend itself to a dramatic acting-out, which will be something of a cross between a dance and a dramatization; the interest and creativity of the children will determine in which direction it might go. The nest as a center, the finding of food, the greeting, all of these can be made part of a sequence that is simple or complex according to the age of the children.

6. This is also a study which lends itself to writing, either prose about what they have seen or poetry about what they have thought and felt. Perhaps the group would like to make a little book of ant stories or ant poems which they have written and illustrated.

BOOKS FOR THE CHILDREN'S USE

Children's Books About Ants

Bronson, Wilfred S. *The Wonder World of the Ants*. Harcourt.
This comprehensive story of life in an ant colony will answer many questions of fact which the children might ask.

Doering, Harold, and McCormick, Mary Jo. *An Ant Is Born*. Sterling.
One of the best, with its clear large photographs and its useful captions. *Natural History* says of it, "A treasure of a book!"

Shuttleworth, Dorothy. *The Story of Ants*. Doubleday.
A fascinating and most excellent book, with insects drawn larger than life size to show detail but including another drawing to show real size. This should be in every classroom library, along with the Doering and McCormick book.

Wheat, G. Collins. *The World of Ants*. Golden Press.
Not as valuable as the above, but clear pictures show twenty-two species of ants, and the book is inexpensive.

Adult Books About Ants

> Goetsch, William. *The Ants.* University of Michigan.
> This book, in the Ann Arbor Science Paperbacks, will give the adult much information and will prove fascinating reading.

SONGS AND POEMS TO USE

There are the familiar Aesop fables, but none of the reference books used for poetry and music for this series of experiences includes ants. For this reason the children's own booklets have been suggested among the activities.

STORY TO SUMMARIZE THE EXPERIENCE

WHAT DO ANTS DO?

ONE EARLY SPRING DAY, Alan was digging tunnels in the sand. He thought about the beetles that tried to make tunnels into his cherry tree and the earthworms and moles that tunneled into the ground.

He watched an ant crawl along the side of the sandbox and wondered if it used a tunnel to reach its home. Why were there so many ants? Some on the tree, some on the ground, and even sometimes ants in the kitchen. Some of them were large and black, some were tiny and red. This was a middle-sized black ant.

Alan remembered seeing one of his friends step on an ant. "Bad old ants!" she had said as she did it. But she didn't seem to know why they were bad. Alan raised his hand to brush the ant off the sandbox, but at that moment he saw the ant pick up a dead mosquito. "Now what is he going to do with that?" Alan wondered. "Will he eat it?"

The ant turned around and started back the way it had come on the side of the sandbox, carrying the mosquito over its head. It seemed to know just where it was going. Alan watched it, still lifting the mosquito out of its way, as it crawled over and around blades of grass or even under them: for now it seemed to be headed toward the garden.

Before Alan could find out where the ant was going his mother called him into the house for supper. Perhaps he could find another one to watch tomorrow.

At the table there was a lot of talking, as usual, but finally Alan had a chance to ask his father, "What do ants do?"

"Well," said his father, "what would you say ants do, Mother?"

"Sometimes they get into my kitchen," said Mrs. Terry. "I don't like that. But I don't really know very much about ants. I'll have to read about them so I can tell you, Alan."

Jim, the oldest brother, who was in high school, said he knew there were a great many different kinds of ants and that they did very different things.

Tom said, "There are army ants and farmer ants, at least. The farmer ants get sweet juice of some kind off the little aphid bugs that live on flowers. They stroke the aphids to make them give out the juice, sort of the way farmers milk cows. We saw pictures of it at school."

Jim told about carpenter ants. He said they helped to prevent forest fires by chewing up the dead trees that lie on the ground. He said dead trees catch fire and burn easily so it was important to have them chewed into tiny bits to become part of the ground as soon as possible.

"But sometimes carpenter ants get into the wood in houses or fence posts. That isn't so good. They don't care where they find dead wood to chew!" said Jim.

"Do they eat the wood?" asked Alan.

"I believe ants only eat the juice of things," said Mr. Terry. "Dead insects, bits of plants or fruit. There are harvester ants that gather seeds and make a kind of bread of them."

"I want to know about the ones that live in our yard," explained Alan.

"Let's find out what kind they are," suggested Mr. Terry. "Tomorrow is Saturday. We can begin by seeing who can find an ant nest first. Then we may be able to decide what kind of ants we have here."

It was Ann who found the first ant nest. It was more like an ant city.

She found it by watching an ant go under a flat stone near the corner of the house. This stone had been there for a long time, but none of the children had known it was the roof of an ant city. The sun had been shining on it when Ann found it and the warm stone had brought a large shiny black ant up to take a heat bath. Ann saw this one plainly when she lifted the stone, but the large ant hurried into a hole and disappeared. Some tiny white things like grains of rice were lying under the warm stone, but now small black ants hastily carried them down out of sight. Some larger ants, but not as big as the first one, appeared and stood guard over the hole.

Ann called her mother and father. The other children heard her call and came too. She told the whole family what she had seen when she lifted the stone.

"Great!" said Mr. Terry. "That biggest ant was probably the queen and the white things were cocoons holding baby ants. The ones in charge of saving the babies were workers and those by the hole are guards. If we want to see the whole city we'll have to destroy it, I'm sorry to say. But they can build another one soon and we won't hurt the ants."

"Wait, wait," urged Mrs. Terry. "I have a surprise. When I did my marketing yesterday I stopped at the library. I found a book that tells how we can make a new home for these ants and move them inside to watch and study. Ann's colony will be fine for this because her ants are large enough to see easily through a glass house."

Ann replaced the stone and all of the Terrys went indoors to see the book. They found the ants in the backyard were Argentines, a kind of ant that came to our country from Argentina in South America. Then they looked at all the ant house designs in the book and decided to use the easiest plan. All they would need was a large-mouthed glass jar with a piece of cheese cloth held on by a rubber band as a cover. In addition to the dirt which would go into the jar there would have to be a flat-bottomed stone to serve as the roof over the hole the ant family would make when they moved in, and two small sponges for drinking water.

Tom found a board that had been the bottom of a box.

Then, as the book told him to do, he made a little wall around the edge of it with plaster of paris powder. The inside of the wall was smooth and straight so ants couldn't escape by climbing it. They set the jar in the middle of this little yard, which was sixteen inches across in each direction.

The next morning the whole family went outdoors with a trowel and a spade; they also took three large spoons and several wide-mouthed jelly jars with tops, a paper bag to hold dirt, and a large sheet of white paper.

Ann was allowed to lift the stone. It was again a warm day and the queen ant was again warming herself under the stone. Quickly and gently Mr. Terry scooped her up with the large spoon he had ready in his hand and into one of the jars she went. Her delicate body looked almost as if it were made of black glass and he was careful not to injure her.

Tom and his mother held the other large spoons and they scooped up the white cocoon babies that were lying under the stone before the worker ants could carry them down through the hole. These went into a separate jar. Workers were placed in a third jar with some of the guards who appeared to protect their entrance hole.

Now Mr. Terry laid the large white paper on the ground right beside the ant house and began to dig carefully down the passages until he came to crowds of ants. Each scoop of dirt was poured onto the paper. First he uncovered a nursery full of nurse workers and babies. Some of the workers had white specks in their jaws. These the children knew from the book were eggs or larvae. The workers, whether or not they were carrying babies, were placed in the workers' jar and then the larvae and cocoons that were left went into the jar already holding some babies.

In the meantime Ann and Alan were capturing workers that came back to the nest from food gathering, because they were a special kind of worker that would also be needed in a new ant city. Soon a room was found containing another queen and her attendants, the workers who took care of her. She was placed with the first queen and her helpers were put among the workers. There were now about fifteen workers in the first jar so a second jar was needed, since the book had warned against crowding the ants. When there were about the same number in the second jar, Mr. Terry began to replace the dirt to make the hole as much the same as it was before as he could. Any remaining ants would soon restore their city under the stone. He kept enough of the dirt to fill the paper bag, however, for he wanted the same dirt for the glass house that the ants had used before. One queen was left to help restore the old nest.

Bits of grass and leaves and damp earth were placed in the jars with the ants. During this time, Jim had been doing a special job. He had rescued any other little bugs or beetles found in the ant city. He had placed them in a little jar by themselves because they were used by the ants as pets or were needed for some other reason.

Now it was easy to fill the jar waiting indoors with dirt from the paper bag. They filled it up to within two inches of the top and placed the two little wet sponges inside and the flat-bottomed rock on top of the dirt against one side of the jar so the ants could start their tunneling under it near to the glass where the tunnel could be seen.

The workers were turned out into the yard around the jar, and they were given the cocoons, larvae, and eggs to take care of. The queens and the other bugs were kept prisoners in their jars until the workers discovered the new place to make a nest and began to get it ready. Tom wanted to make it easy for the workers to find the dirt-filled jar, so he made a little path up to the jar with a piece of paper folded to hook over the top.

It wasn't long before three of the scurrying, exploring workers made their way up the paper path and found the dirt in the jar. By the next day the new nest was being built under the rock in the jar, and the children allowed the two queens and the bugs from the old nest to be placed in the jar. Then the fun of watching a complete ant city began.

Ann and Alan took charge of feeding the ants, and Tom was responsible for seeing that the earth in the jar was just moist enough and the drinking sponges always wet.

In the weeks that followed Alan learned what ants do. He learned about Argentine ants by watching them, and about the other kinds from the book his mother read to him. Now when he saw an ant walking through the grass he knew it was following along an odor trail. He knew that when it met another ant it would either greet a friend with touching antennae or fight an enemy with strong jaws and a spray of acid. These he knew were its only weapons. He knew now that ants make the soil richer by the plant and dead insect material they bury in it, and that they lead busy lives, and are needed by the plants and creatures around them. The tree needed them, and so did the garden and the grass, just as much as the insect-eating birds and animals.

Alan found he was watching what happened on the ground just as much as what happened in the tree these days — especially what happened in the grass.

INTRODUCTION TO THE EXPERIENCE TO FOLLOW

After reading "What Do Ants Do?" the next experience may be introduced in some such way as this:

> "We know some of the creatures that live in the grass
> and some that live under it. But how much do we
> know about the grass itself?"

The obvious answers will be: its color, how it grows, where it is. A new direction of thought can be opened by the question "Who eats the grass?"

The leader may suggest that next time they all put their information about grass together and see how much they do know about it, including the subject of grass as food. If they wish, the children could bring with them pictures of animals that eat grass, or even some of the animals themselves. Guinea pigs and rabbits could certainly be entertained in the classroom.

EXPERIENCE WITH

Grass

DEVELOPING THE EXPERIENCE

WHEN THE CHILDREN began their first adventure study, they discovered differences in soil by digging into the ground. This gave them some background for the present exploration of grass and the topsoil it holds together. It may be better this time to let the subject of soil come into focus incidentally, first turning attention to grass as a food.

"Who eats grass?" begins the teacher's inquiry. For this time the children have been challenged to provide the information. When a list of grasseaters has grown long enough to satisfy the class, a second question can be asked, "Are there different kinds of grass, and if so, what are they?"

Fields of tall grass or of grain may not be available to visit, although it is best to go to these if at all possible. But pictures will be available. The pictures should be on the walls, and the children given plenty of time during the discussion of grasseaters to make the discovery of variety for themselves. The children will then have to decide whether or not wheat and other grains are grass.

Now is a good time to plant some grains and some grass seed so the children can see for themselves how similar the early stages of growth will be. (*Making and Using Classroom Science Ma-*

terials has a number of suggestions of different ways in which seed can be germinated in the classroom.) If the class can go to a grain and seed store with glass jars ready and a set of labels, they can secure samples of all the available kinds. The teacher will, of course, make arrangements for this ahead of time. When planting has been done, the remaining seeds can be used in making decorative charts on colored paper upon which seeds can be mounted as they are listed or glued in solid designs opposite their names. (No attempt should be made with children this age to make the more elaborate seed mosaics; they are not ready for this.) Grass seed can head the list, properly named as to its variety.

Now man's name will have to be added to the list of grass-eaters, and it will be fun for the children to imagine ways in which people may have first found out that good food could be made from grain. A frieze or mural can be painted to illustrate their own imaginings as to how the discovery was made, or it can be dramatized with a family of nomadic people as the characters in the drama. In this story the use of fire will have to be introduced, changing the nature of grass food from the form in which other mammals eat it; but man's name belongs on the list, nevertheless, as the children will agree.

"But what else does man eat?" the teacher will now ask, for she is still helping the children do their own learning. As they answer the questions they will begin to realize that man is both a primary and a secondary eater of grass, since he uses grazing animals for meat. Soon they should be helped to discover, if they do not realize it spontaneously, that, except for the products of the sea, all of our food comes from the soil, directly or indirectly. With this discovery the children are well started on the concept of human dependence upon other forms of life. Here is material for years of thought, and too much unsought information at this time could block the way to future exploration. An avenue has been opened, and if young children catch a brief glimpse of all that is to be found at the other end, they will be able to follow it further some day.

A logical sequence to these inquiries is the cooking of food made with flour or butter or both. A cake can be mixed and while it is baking each ingredient can be traced to its original source. (Do not use a cake mix; really make a cake!) In some regions a flour mill can be visited, and in any case the children will enjoy trying to make a little flour or cornmeal the primitive way, grinding and pounding it with stones.

In a quiet moment after the self-prepared feast, it may be possible to lead the children's thinking from the food into the soil itself. "Where did the plant get the grain that made this flour? What is it made from? Does the soil hold the ingredients? Without the plant could man make food out of soil and water, air and sunshine?"

The wise leader will not answer the questions after asking them, but will, in addition, let each question come out of the answer given to the one before. If all the learnings planned do not take place they can be used for some other occasion when they may arise more naturally. Do not push the children to verbalize the concepts which are involved; at this age it is enough if they sense them and respond to the discussion.

When the story, "The Green Grass Carpet," is read, later, a part of the answer will be apparent in the description of the way the soil is renewed by dead organic matter. So there will be opportunity in the discussion of the story to pursue some of these matters. In discussion of the renewal of the soil the phrase "nothing was wasted" is used. Disgust at decay and "waste" matter is common to all children, but it will begin to disappear as this concept grows. Before the next planting is done, bone meal and manure should be used as fertilizer to give opportunity to help them restate the process of soil enrichment by the giving back of materials that helped one life to grow, and may now be used again to nurture new life.

When the children are old enough to grasp the whole concept of this "giving back" that assists the continuity of life they will be basing their mature acceptance of the cycle of living and dying upon these early experiences, whether or not they are consciously remembered. Let the discussion be leisurely, so that these complex ideas can "sink in" slowly, and do not push it.

OTHER POSSIBLE EXPERIENCES WITH GRASS AND TOPSOIL

1. An interesting class project would be the purchase of one of the tiny plastic "greenhouses" in which cactus seeds are already planted and ready to grow. For children not familiar with the desert this new form of "green growing things" will be a valuable experience. If not available locally they are found in many gift catalogs (the mail order variety).

2. If the cacti are raised a brief introduction to the desert could take a class session. *Tia Maria's Garden* (Viking) or *Elf Owl* (Viking) or both can be used. The children can then imagine the Terrys moving to the desert, building a sandbox under a saguaro, and see if they can figure out what things Ann and Alan might have found there. (Desert children can reverse the process, imagining evergreens and moss-covered ground cover.)

3. If the imaginary "move" is made, it might lead to a class correspondence with a class in such a location for the exchange of mounted samples of grass, leaves, cones, or other regional things, as well as pictures drawn by the children themselves. This will help widen their view both of their own land and of others like themselves.

4. If a place is available for such activity, the grass can be removed from a square foot or so of soil, and water played on both the now bare area, and a grassy area, to show the children that grass really does "hold the soil" in place. Or a trip can be made to a spot where there has been serious erosion. The recognition of such places once learned tends to make anyone much more aware of the serious erosion which is occurring in all of our communities. Many children will have seen plantings by highways, without knowing they have a useful purpose as well as adding to the beauty. Conservation principles cannot be introduced too early, nor mentioned too often!

5. *Snipp, Snapp, Snurr, and the Buttered Bread* (Whitman), by Maj Lindman, clearly pictures the cycle of sun and growing things and our dependence on the grass.

BOOKS FOR THE CHILDREN'S USE

Children's Books About Grass

> Blough, Glenn O. *Who Lives in the Meadow?* Whittlesey
> (McGraw)
>
> Through exploring a meadow one learns how many
> creatures adapt to their environment. Excellent illustra-
> tions.
>
> Kane, Henry B. *The Tale of a Meadow.* Knopf.
>
> This is a particularly sensitive and beautiful book of a
> boy who knows and loves the things of the meadow.
> Illustrations as sensitive as the text.
>
> Lubbell, Winifred and Cecil. *The Tall Grass Zoo.* Rand
> McNally.
>
> An imaginative book that presents the variety of things
> which are living in the grass, and the interrelationships
> which exist between them.
>
> Uhle, Melvin J. *About Grasses, Grains and Canes.* Mel-
> mont.
>
> Useful for clear illustrations, although the content is
> crowded and pedestrian. But little is available in this
> area which is more imaginative, and this is sound in
> detail.

SONGS AND POEMS TO USE

"Topsoil": Number 65 in *We Sing of Life.*

STORY TO SUMMARIZE THE EXPERIENCE

THE GREEN GRASS CARPET

ALL AROUND the cherry tree and the sandbox, grass covered the
backyard like a green carpet. It began by the back steps and
spread out as far as the vegetable and flower garden. The children liked to walk on the grass with bare feet on hot days. It felt
cool and soft and tickly. In the early morning it felt a little bit
wet. On each blade of grass a drop of dew hung sparkling in the
sunshine.

The Terry children liked to sit on the green grass carpet
too. Sometimes in summer they ate lunch on the lawn in a shady

place. When Alan and Ann were younger they had taken their naps on an old bedspread laid on the grass in a cool corner of the yard. The grass was fine for games; if you fell down you landed on a soft green cushion.

But Tom, who often had to mow the lawn, got very tired of his job. One evening he complained.

"I don't see why we water the grass to make it grow better, and then have to cut it all the time because it grows so fast!" he grumbled.

"It would die without water, of course," his mother replied. "How would you like a backyard covered with nothing but mud? In summer our house would be filled with dust when the dry winds blew across the yard, and whenever it rained we would have to wade in mud."

"The topsoil would all blow away in time," remarked Mr. Terry from behind his evening newspaper.

"What's topsoil?" Ann and Alan asked at the same time. They were on the rug playing with Mrs. Cat and her kittens.

Their father laid his newspaper down.

"Topsoil is the rich layer of dirt on top of the ground. Under it you find hard clay or rock. Topsoil is the layer that holds plant food and water for seeds to grow in. Grass roots grow deep enough and long enough to tie every little particle of top soil in place so the wind and sun can't dry it and turn it to dust."

"Well, we do need the grass I guess, but I wish we could have a goat or a sheep to keep it short then," said Tom.

"Or a horse," suggested Ann hopefully.

"Or a cow," said Mrs. Terry laughing. "Then we could have our own cream and milk and make our own butter."

Mr. Terry was looking out the window and thinking.

"Whenever you eat a peanut butter sandwich or drink a glass of milk, your lunch comes from topsoil. Without grass, how hungry we would be!"

In the late fall the green grass back of the house turned brown and seemed to die. But snow covered it during much of the winter and whenever the snow melted there was green grass under it. The thick web of grass roots holding the topsoil together held enough melted snow water to keep the grass alive.

In the spring the Terry children were glad to see a green lawn to play on again. They didn't know that in one summer their grass would grow miles and miles of root, covered with miles of fine root hairs. Some of these roots would die and make a sponge of rotting fiber in the topsoil, putting back into the ground the chemicals that made them grow when they were alive.

They did know that insects and worms and little animals that tunneled through the spongy earth sometimes died in the ground, adding their tiny bodies to become part of the topsoil again. Even the castings of the worms and the unneeded food that passed through the bodies of animals enriched the topsoil so that nothing was wasted. The topsoil under the grass gave back to the grass what it had to have to grow, and the grass became food for new live creatures.

As Mr. Terry planted some grass seed to cover a bare place in the yard that summer, he sang the new line the children had added to their song:

"Soil needs grass, and grass needs soil."

But there was too much to sing about grass. When they tried to put everything into the song that needed grass and topsoil, the children had given up.

"We never can say it all," Tom explained. "Everything that walks or flies or hops or crawls on the earth needs the soil or what grows in it."

Already the Terry children had found that you couldn't put into one song all the life there was going on in one backyard.

There was the garden for instance, with all its visitors!

INTRODUCTION TO THE EXPERIENCE TO FOLLOW

"Do other plants help hold topsoil as well as grass?"

"What other plants do we need?"

After the experience with grass, a plan can be discussed for planting a small garden of flowers and vegetables. In climates where it will have to be done indoors the use of someone's home greenhouse, or a warm sunny garage or basement, will be preferable to the classroom unless the plants can be tended there daily, watered, and left undisturbed. Each child should be allowed to choose his own seed package, with some guidance to avoid the choice of a plant that takes too long or is too difficult to grow in such circumstances.

EXPERIENCE WITH

The Garden

DEVELOPING THE EXPERIENCE

JUNE, JULY, AND AUGUST may be the months when the leader and the group of children can no longer be together; and in many parts of the country these are the months when the usual flower and vegetable garden grows to maturity. For this reason, the experience with a garden must be carefully planned to begin as early in the spring as possible. In places where March is too early for outdoor planting, seed boxes, cold frames, and greenhouses can be used. In addition to this, a wise leader will try to provide for planting flowers and vegetables that mature rapidly.

Those boys and girls who wish to plant flowers may get the best quick indoor results from bulbs of spring-blooming plants. Those choosing to grow vegetables should join in some research to discover which will be ready for use before the end of the school year. A display of brightly colored bulb and seed packages showing many varieties can be the basis for choice and decision. On the back of each one will appear information as to the kind of soil needed, the time for planting, and when maturity can be expected. Radishes and lettuce planted in March should be ready for an elegant salad luncheon in May.

If soil has been a subject of inquiry earlier, the children will be intelligently interested in finding whatever is needed for their small gardens. Sandy soil, the easiest to dig up in early spring, because it warms sooner than silty or clay loams, can be enriched with humus in the form of peat moss, leaf mold, compost material, or stable manure. If the class wishes to be really scientific, samples of soil can be taken to a county or state experiment station for testing. Advice will be given there on how to correct or increase acidity in the soil tested if either action needs to be taken.

If indoor planting is decided upon, clean containers should be used providing drainage through holes in the bottom. A layer of gravel, cinders, or pieces of broken flower pots is recommended above the holes. The soil should be sifted. Usually equal parts of loam, sand, and leaf mold will be satisfactory soil for starting seed. No fertilizer is needed. The surface should be level for uniform watering. Planting should be done as directed on the seed package. A sunny window is necessary for the location of the seed flats.

If a home greenhouse is not available for use, a cold frame may take its place. Seed can be sown in a cold frame a full month before it can be placed in the open ground. A window sash makes a fine top for a cold frame, and the supporting frame is easy to build. Small gardens often have a frame 6 × 6 feet, requiring 2 3 × 6 window sashes for cover. Such a cold frame should be placed in a sheltered spot with a southern exposure where it will get full sun. The back (north) side should be 12 to 15 inches high, with the south side about 4 inches shorter so the glass will slope. If made of wood, the sides and ends should be an inch thick and sunk into the ground to a depth of 6 inches. More permanent cold frames are made of thicker wood or concrete about $2\frac{1}{2}$ inches thick. Cold frames are best filled with a mixture of well prepared soil from 4 to 6 inches deep, with equal parts of leaf mold, garden soil, and sand.

One excellent way to insure success in planting a garden is to secure the expert advice and help of the best gardener in the neighborhood. Children benefit from getting to know men and women who have special skills and knowledge. Finding the right person to help with this experience can be very important indeed. It is in the care of the garden, its watering, weeding, and nursing along that the children will come to feel real ownership and concern for their own little plot and experience pride in results. If the gardener resource person lives nearby, he can assist in supervising when children visit the garden and care for their plantings between meetings of the group.

Gardens suggest many activities such as the sprouting of seeds in cotton so the first growth process can be watched. (It is usually below ground and therefore not seen.) There is also interest in viewing films that show plant growth speeded up so it is visible. Or in making field trips to professional greenhouses or to markets where fresh flowers and vegetables are displayed; in visiting stores where all kinds of garden tools and gadgets are sold; and in painting pictures of flowers and vegetables with real ones to examine before the painting is done.

Children enjoy "being" seeds and growing up to music selected to suggest sunshine and rain. When fully grown they sway in the breeze together. This sometimes leads to "dying" and falling to the ground again, when it can be remembered that a plant becomes part of the soil to enrich it for the growth of its own seeds; and so the child "being" the plant goes on growing up again from seed position to full height and then down again until the continuity of the life cycle is really felt.

If Easter comes during the weeks when the garden experience is going on, it will have new meaning for children who are enjoying the role of gardener in such a group as this. Although Easter may mean far more than the "return of spring," this return is a symbol of it which children can appreciate.

OTHER POSSIBLE EXPERIENCES WITH A GARDEN

1. It may be possible, after consultation with the persons in charge of the building where the children meet, to do some actual permanent planting that the children can feel is theirs for years to come. This should be made a "very special" occasion for the children if it is done, with perhaps some adults and babies there to tie the generations together.

2. If some of the children can plan home gardens, or the parents

can be urged to make window boxes available for those who do not have planting space, this is an experience that can go with the children into their summer vacation.

3. *Making and Using Classroom Science Materials,* pages 74 through 88, contains many practical suggestions and projects that will be useful in connection with the study of a garden.

4. Growing bulbs to be shared with shut-ins can be a real experience in giving for the children. Because it is so hard to share these when they are about to burst into bloom the children will have an experience in *really* giving "of their own." Do not spoil the richness of this giving by raising an extra bulb for each child and thus take the edge off of the giving. (This does not mean that they might not raise bulbs earlier or later.)

5. Gardens, their growing, and flowers are provocative of many thoughts for the writing of poems; and some of the poems can be made into songs. By now the children's writing may begin to show whether or not they are grasping and expressing the idea of the interdependence of all living things. The teacher will be alert to watch for these ideas to check on the effectivness of what is being done, but will not point them out to the children.

BOOKS FOR THE CHILDREN'S USE

Children's Books About Gardens and Flowers

> Guilcher, J. M. and Noailles. *A Fruit Is Born.* Sterling.
> Another in this most excellent series of books which should be in every class library, from flower to seed, illustrated with beautiful and detailed photographs.
> Hutchins, Ross E. *This Is a Flower.* Dodd.
> How flowers serve to continue plant life, how they attract insects, and how they serve to delight man as well.
> Jordan, Helene J. *How a Seed Grows.* Crowell.
> A simple book, with a simple experiment, but it will be useful either for the younger children, or to be taken home and the work done there.
> Schneider, Herman and Nina. *Plants in the City.* Day.
> Experiments in indoor gardening which are truly in-

teresting to carry out and are particularly planned for
city dwellers.

Selsam, Millicent E. *Seeds and More Seeds*. Harper.
A young child's experiences with seeds and plants,
simple but useful.

Watson, Aldred. *My Garden Grows*. Viking.
Accurate and beautiful pictures of growing vegetables,
along with useful information.

Zion, Gene. *The Plant Sitter*. Harper.
Shows how one can grow plants from cuttings, and is
interesting in its presentation. This is an activity not so
often used with children and should provoke real interest.

SONGS AND POEMS TO USE

"In the Garden": Number 65 in *We Sing of Life*.
"Spring Has Now Unwrapped the Flowers": Number 167 in
We Sing of Life.
"This Is the Way": Number 37 in *Martin and Judy Songs*.
"Look": Number 21 in *Martin and Judy Songs*.

STORY TO SUMMARIZE THE EXPERIENCE

"GARDENS AREN'T FOR PLAYING . . ."

WHEN YOU WENT around the Terrys' house into the backyard,
first you saw the grassy lawn with the cherry tree and the sandbox at one side. Then back beyond the grass was the garden.
The garden covered the far end of the backyard. The children
had to be careful not to let their balls go back into the garden. A
baseball might break off something important growing there.

"Gardens aren't for playing," Ann explained to her friends
when they came over to have fun in her yard. Then she would
take them for a walk through the garden to show them her part
of it, and they would go back to the grass and the tree and the
sandbox to play.

There were two kinds of important things growing in the
garden, flowers and vegetables. The flowers were certainly the
prettiest and they smelled the sweetest. However, the vegetables

were good to eat: sweet corn, tomatoes, carrots, radishes, and lettuce. In their own way they were beautiful too.

Each of the younger Terry children had a planting place in the garden. They could choose in the spring whether they wanted it on the flower side or the vegetable side, and then they could decide what kind of flower or vegetable they wanted to grow and care for through the summer.

Whenever Mrs. Terry wanted some radishes for supper she would call Alan, who always planted radishes. He would run out to the garden and walk carefully along a path between radishes and lettuce plants looking for strong, fully grown radishes to pull. The round red balls were usually pushing up out of the ground a little if they were ready to eat. If Alan pulled up a radish too small for eating he quickly planted it again so it would keep on growing.

The round red radish was the root of the plant. It had grown fat and good to eat from the water it had soaked up from the soil. This water was full of the kind of plant food a radish needs. The water was there because of earthworm tunnels and ant burrows, because of rain and sprinkler water. The green top of the plant, especially the leaves, made a kind of sugar out of sunshine and air and the soil water from below. This sugar made by the green leaves gave all the parts of the plant what they needed to live and grow. Alan's father had explained this to him, but he still wondered where the red color came from that covered the crisp white radish balls.

Alan was proud of his radishes because he had fixed the soil, planted the seeds, pulled out weeds that came up in the radish bed, and watered the plants with the sprinkler when there wasn't enough rain.

Ann had grown flowers in her part of the garden. She liked to pick bouquets to take to school for her teacher, or to give to her grandmother who lived nearby. Mrs. Terry had her own flowers in the garden, but sometimes she asked for some special kind from Ann's garden.

"I need some white daisies," she said one day. "I have blue larkspur in a bowl for the dinner table, but they will look prettier with a few daisies mixed in here and there."

Ann ran out to pick some for her mother. She was proud of her daisies because she had fixed the soil, planted the seeds, pulled out weeds that came up in the daisy bed, and watered the plants with the sprinkler when there wasn't enough rain.

Most of the vegetables were from Mr. Terry's part of the garden. Tom and Jim had helped him take care of it, but each of them had his own vegetable too. Tom had grown cabbages and Jim had planted carrots. Mr. Terry was very proud of his red tomatoes and the sweet corn which was the whole family's favorite all through the summer. Whenever they enjoyed corn-on-the-cob for dinner all the Terrys were glad their father and the older boys had worked long and hard keeping this part of the garden in fine condition.

Birds helped to keep the garden too. They ate bugs and insects that sometimes ate the plants. Once in a while a robin would taste a tomato if it happened to grow close to the ground where he was worm-hunting, but no one minded that. He had been helping by eating fat caterpillars that chewed tomato leaves.

The garden fed many kinds of insects and caterpillars. It also fed the hummingbirds and the bees. It fed a rabbit who sometimes came to visit at night. It fed some of the neighbor families, too, because the children often surprised their friends with presents of lettuce or tomatoes or radishes.

"Gardens aren't for playing," Ann had said, and she was right. They were for working and for enjoying and for sharing. The Terrys' garden was for visiting, too, and not only by family and friends. It had many visitors the children never saw, like the rabbit who came at night. Some of its insect visitors came and went all day almost as if it were their garden.

It was some time before the children learned that they would have no sweet corn or tomatos to enjoy, no flower seeds to gather in the fall for next year's planting, without some of the insect visitors who were working among them.

After they had adventures with two of these garden visitors they discovered that gardens are for learning, too, because the caterpillars and the bees taught them some things they had not known before.

INTRODUCTION TO THE EXPERIENCE TO FOLLOW

Following the reading of the story "Gardens Aren't for Playing . . . ," either the experience with the caterpillar and the butterfly, or the experience with bees can follow quite naturally. If the gardens have been outdoors during the blooming of flowers and the maturing of leafy vegetables, the presence of bees and caterpillars will be noticed. Anyone helping with the children's garden should be warned against spraying or destroying the caterpillar visitors. However, if they are causing too much damage, they can be "captured" and saved for the children's next session. A few should be left on the plants to be found by the children.

EXPERIENCE WITH

Bees

DEVELOPING THE EXPERIENCE

EVIDENCE OF MAN'S EARLY INTEREST in bees appears in many parts of the world. In 385–295 B.C. a Greek coin was engraved with the detailed outlines of a bee. Wall paintings of honeybees are found in ancient graves in Egypt, and a rock painting at least 7,000 years old in Spain shows an artist's record of the taking of honey from a beehive. Other ancient writings besides those in the Old Testament also refer to honey and to the industry of bees.

Our folklore, poetry, song, and prose are full of delightful stories and tributes to the powers and abilities of the bee. Children's libraries abound with factual and fictional accounts of bees and their doings.

In case there may be among the children of an exploring class a boy or girl who has been stung at some time, the leader will do well to make use of the first sight of a bee to advise standing still, listening, and watching. This will avoid the mischance of anyone's striking out in panic and frightening or angering the insect so harmlessly intent upon its work. It will lead to the first awareness on the part of many children of what a small and interesting creature a bee is. (Should any child in the group have a serious allergy to bee-sting, it is assumed that the parents would have so informed the leader before enrolling him in such a wide-ranging outdoor program. It may be good, however, to have the parents understand that bees are to be included, and to be assured that all needed precautions will be taken.)

Such a brief encounter can be followed by the study of a piece of honeycomb in the classroom. Books can be passed around, looked at, read, and enjoyed. Pictures can be examined and beeswax introduced. Finally, the honey can be served and eaten on crackers or toast.

By now the children will have sufficient background to really watch the field activity of bees if they are observable in the area. Ideally they will visit an apiary and see much of what they have heard and read about the bees as it actually happens. This observation, under the direction of an expert, will have more meaning if there has been previous closeup examination of photographs and detailed drawings. In studying nearly every species of animal, attention must be paid to its enemies, which also serve to keep the species from multiplying in number to the point where food becomes scarce and the whole race suffers. Bees have robber enemies. Their guards are alert to protect the hive, not only from robber bees, which sometimes come from other colonies, but from such contrasting animals as mice and bears. Bears have such thick coats that bee-stings are not a deterrent, and they often destroy the homes of wild bees; but a mouse can be killed by bee-stings. If this happens inside the hive so the bees cannot remove the dead mouse, its whole body is covered with "propolis," the bee glue used among other things for fastening the cells of the honeycomb together.

If a bee colony's store of honey is stolen, the entire colony may not be able to survive the winter. Man can be an enemy in this way, but wise beekeepers and all people aware of the importance of bees in agriculture will take only a portion of the honey, leaving enough for the bees.

Praying mantises, wasps, some flying birds, and chickens are also the enemies of bees, eating them or, in the case of wasps, sucking the honey from their honey sacs.

When a bee stings in defense the sting remains in the victim's flesh, and the bee is wounded by its removal from her own body. Within a few days the bee herself will die.

These dramas in the life of the bee may be revealed to the children by the books into which their questions will lead the group. The fate of the drones is certain to cause discussion. In fact there is so much content to the story of the life of bees that it may be hard to leave this experience behind and turn to another one without spending a longer time on it than most of the previous experiences. The wise leader will remember that this is not the only time the children will meet the bee, and therefore the leader will not feel that everything in this fascinating life needs to be covered this time.

Children can make candles if the leader is able to find in candle specialty departments the sheets of beeswax manufactured in Canada and widely sold in this country. (They may also be ordered with instruction booklets from American Handicrafts Company, 4 East Sixteenth Street, New York, N.Y. 10003. A catalog should be secured first to find current prices and the wide range of materials available.) Churches frequently use beeswax candles for religious services because they do not bend in warm rooms and are less apt to smoke and smell when burning.

Tailors use pieces of beeswax for the waxing of thread, and specimens of this may be secured from them or their suppliers. It is also used as a base in the making of many cosmetic creams.

Children will enjoy tasting and seeing a variety of kinds of honey, since flavor and color vary depending upon the flower from which the nectar is taken. They can imagine how its sweetness was first discovered by primitive man, and will be glad that it contains important minerals as well as sugar. Things that taste as good as honey are not always good for one as well!

There are other kinds of bees than honeybees, and the handsome, clumsy bumblebee is apt to become a favorite. Indeed, children digging in the early spring may open the winter nest of a bumblebee queen and discover her (perhaps in a field mouse's house) surviving the winter and raising a family to become the next summer's colony. Bumblebees, with the exception of the queen, die at the end of the flower season. In her winter nest the queen makes wax cells, lays eggs, and stores honey for her own food and for her babies as they develop. Bumblebees are often found around red clover, which yields its nectar only to strong insects.

Children may be interested to learn that there are bees without stings in the tropics, some of them as small as mosquitoes and some as large as the honeybees. They defend themselves with tiny biting jaws.

They will also find the solitary bees interesting, such as the carpenter bee so enchantingly described in Jean George's *Hole in a Tree*. Other bees that do not live in colonies are the miner bee, the mason bee, as well as the leaf-cutter bee that makes its nest from bits of leaves glued together to form containers resembling capsules.

Among the children's stories which can be enjoyed and dramatized into games about bees are *The Bumblebee's Secret* by Miriam Schlein (Abelard), and the story about the little boy who couldn't get the goats out of the field, found in many anthologies including *Bookhouse*.

Some of the children may become interested in finding out about man-made beehives in different parts of the world, drawing them or making replicas of clay.

The hexagonal shape of the bee's waxen cell suggests designs for a display of drawings, paintings, or clay modelings done by the children during their experience with bees.

If the leader has a favorite baking recipe making use of honey, or knows a mother who has one, a kitchen party can conclude the study and may be the right place for reading the summarizing story, "Bees in the Garden."

OTHER POSSIBLE EXPERIENCES WITH BEES

1. Pages 53 and 54 in *Making and Using Classroom Science Materials* tell how a simple observation hive can be made for the classroom, or you may have a natural-history museum nearby where there is one already established. These are fascinating to watch, and many of the activities described in books about bees can be readily seen in the observation hive.

2. Children should have an opportunity, perhaps after seeing some pictures the leader has mounted of bees in flight, to listen

to Rimski-Korsakov's "The Flight of the Bumblebee" and then discuss what they have heard in the music. This is not a good record to try to dance to, although occasionally children have worked out interesting patterns to fit the rapid rhythm of the music. But it is most excellent "listening music."

3. If the children have been interested, and they are almost certain to be, in the dances which the bees use in order to communicate with one another, they might be interested in working out simple rhythmic patterns in relation to these. These dances can be seen in an observation hive, and if they have been seen there first, the children will be aware that the bee is *not* performing while the others watch, but is crawling around and over the bees while she does the dance. They, therefore, will discuss their dance and (we hope) decide to simplify it in the process of doing the dance as though the other bees were not there.

4. A discussion of "nonverbal communication" is always valuable for children, and the dances of the bee are a prime example of this. Children are always fascinated with trying to communicate with signs and gestures, and making them more aware of the advantages of verbal communication is always important.

5. If a few bees can be brought into the classroom in a large glass container with flowers and are not kept too long, the children will be fascinated with a chance to examine them closely with magnifying glasses and see that they are indeed like the close-up pictures in some of the books they have been studying.

6. Quiet observation in a garden makes it possible to see the bees actually going from flower to flower, and often to observe the pollen on their legs. After this observation a creative "flower and bee dance" might be done by the children, in contrast to the communication dances which are really done in order to understand better the patterns which the bees use. Dance has many uses, and the leader will not always want to use it in the same way. Or this might be a good time to get a professional dancer to come in to the class and dance a bee dance for the children to enjoy.

7. Bees are often used in design, for jewelry and on textiles. The

children may be able to collect some "bee designs" at home (with the help of their parents) and have an exhibit of these. This might well lead to the making of more interesting drawings and paintings as they get clues to interesting uses of the bee motif.

BOOKS FOR THE CHILDREN'S USE

Children's Books About Bees

Adrian, Mary. *Honeybee.* Holiday.
> The dances done by the honeybee are described in fascinating detail, along with much other information which will help in answering questions.

Doering, Harald. *A Bee Is Born.* Holiday.
> This book is a *must.* Its beautiful close-up photographs, some of them more than life size, are fascinating; and the book contains much information. The pictures alone will answer many questions, and are therefore particularly useful with the younger children.

Foster, Virgil. *Close-up of a Honey Bee.* Young Scott.
> Unusual photographs which will help lead the children to closer observation of the bees they see.

Goudey, Alice E. *Here Come the Bees.* Scribner.
> A life-cycle story of the bees which will add much to the children's comprehension of the on-going nature of all life.

Hawes, Judy. *Bees and Beelines.* Crowell.
> A few added facts, and a good book, although not of the quality of some of the others which are listed.

Neal, Charles D. *What Is a Bee?* Benefic.
> Not equal to *The First Book of Bees,* but attractive and readable. Each of these bee books contains some material that will be new to the group.

Ritchie, Margaret. *Bees.* Beacon.
> This pamphlet in the Beacon Science Series has some very fine photographs and a drawing of the rock painting of primitive man, and, although written for older children, will give the leader additional ideas about myths and stories of bees if the group wants to extend its study.

Schlein, Miriam. *The Bumblebee's Secret.* Abelard.
> As suggested under "Developing the Experience" this is

an excellent story for reading to the group and for dramatization.

Tibbets, Albert B. *The First Book of Bees.* Watts.

This is one of the best of the First Book Series. (They vary greatly in quality.) Information on the dances and a particularly good section on the wide variety of hives that have been used for bees.

Adult Books About Bees

Von Frisch, Karl. *Bees: Their Vision, Chemical Senses and Language.* Cornell.

This is a classic in its field, and no adult can read it without finding much material that will spark a real enthusiasm for the subject.

Von Frisch, Karl. *The Dancing Bees.* Harcourt.

Many experiments through which the knowledge of bees has been obtained are described in this book. With older children the leader may want to give simplified descriptions of some of these.

The National Geographic Magazine for August 1959 has a fascinating article, with both color and black-and-white illustrations, which would be fine for mounting to be used in the classroom. Secondhand bookstores often carry old *Geographics*. They are not hard to obtain.

SONGS AND POEMS TO USE

"Buzz! Buzz!": Number 23 in *Martin and Judy Songs.*

STORY TO SUMMARIZE THE EXPERIENCE

BEES IN THE GARDEN

ONE DAY Ann's mother asked her to pick some daisies for a surprise present for a neighbor who was ill. Ann hurried out to her part of the garden carrying a pair of scissors and a basket. In just a moment she came back to the house, her basket still empty.

"Mother, I can't cut the daisies right now," she said. "There are bees in ever so many of the flowers. I can hear them buzzing and humming everywhere."

"The bees are taking sweet nectar from the flowers this

morning," said Mrs. Terry. "Take the daisies they have passed by and listen to the bee music. Unless you bother a bee it will not bother you."

She went to the garden with Ann and showed her it was fun to stand still and watch a bee at work gathering nectar to use in making honey. The bee's hairy underside got all yellow from a golden powder in the center of the flowers, a powder called "pollen." With her two hind legs the bee scraped the pollen off her body and packed it into a place on each hind leg called a pollen basket. When both "baskets" were full you could see the yellow pollen like balls on the hind legs, ready to be unpacked when the bees got back to the hive. Ann's mother said all the worker bees were females. She said they would mix this pollen with honey to feed to the young bees. She called it "bee bread."

Ann was glad her mother had told her about what the bees were doing, but she asked her to go back to the house so she could cut the daisies all by herself. As she worked she listened to the bee music and wished she could see the baby bees eating bread inside a beehive. But she still wondered if it was good for her flowers to have their nectar and pollen carried away by bees.

When all the family was together around the dinner table that evening Ann asked the questions she had been wondering about all day.

"Is it good for a flower to have bees take the nectar and pollen away from it?"

"It doesn't hurt the flowers at all," said Tom, who had studied about bees in school. "Some flowers need the pollen from another blossom to start seeds growing. The bees often carry pollen from one flower to another. Without knowing it they are helping themselves because this helps new seeds to grow, and when the seeds are ripe and fall to the ground new plants will come up to make new flowers for bees to visit another year."

"Then bees need flowers, and flowers need bees," said Ann.

Not long after this when the Terry children were helping their mother with the marketing they saw a man putting square boxes of honey on a shelf in the store. He had a large carton full of these squares, and he told Mrs. Terry the honey came from his own beehives.

"I wish I could see a beehive," said Ann politely as she watched him stacking the honey. "I watch the bees working in our garden, but I've never seen them in a hive."

Mrs. Terry took a box of honey to put in her grocery cart.

The man introduced himself to her as Mr. Parker of Clover Honey Farm.

"Perhaps you would like to bring the children to visit our farm some day," he said.

When Mrs. Terry saw how eager the children looked she promised she would take them to visit the farm soon. She wrote down directions for reaching the bee farm and thanked Mr. Parker for inviting them.

Ann, Alan, and Tom kept reminding their mother of her promise, so, the first sunny Saturday when all the work at home was done, the family got into the car and headed for Clover Honey Farm. It wasn't hard to find. Fields of sweet-smelling clover surrounded the house, and nearby they saw rows of wooden beehives, painted white, and several small buildings and sheds.

Beside the front gate was a large table where people could buy honey without even leaving their cars if they wished. A boy about Tom's age was in charge of the table. He told Mr. Terry his name was Cliff Parker, and when he heard that the family had come to visit the beehives he ran to call his father.

Mr. Parker recognized the children and Mrs. Terry right away. He smiled as he shook hands all around and welcomed them to Clover Honey Farm.

During the next hour Ann and Alan and Tom learned so much about bees and honey they could hardly wait to tell their friends at home and at school all about it. They saw the inside of several hives where a queen bee had laid eggs in rows of little wax cells made by the bees. The wax came from their own bodies, and the children learned to call it beeswax. They learned that the bees chew the wax to soften it and then shape it into small six-sided containers which they glue together with a sticky juice from the buds of certain trees.

The children saw what a baby bee first looks like, a worm-like white larva that has to be fed bee milk by nurse bees until it is three days old, when it can have bee bread. Mr. Parker told them the bee milk is sour tasting and comes from the foreheads of the nurse bees. If a baby bee is to be a queen she continues to get nothing but bee milk, which is also called "royal jelly."

Every day for five days the babies grow too big for their skin. It pops and comes off, and a new skin covers the growing larva. When it is so fat that it fills the wax cell, the larva spins a cocoon of white silk from its mouth. The worker bees cover the cell with wax, and inside the larva changes slowly for twelve days. By that time a complete little bee is ready to kick its way out of the cocoon and bite a hole in the wax. It comes out, rests, and crawls to one of the feeding cells where thousands of bees are busy storing honey in the same kind of cell the young bee came from.

Mr. Parker knew how to remove trays of honey-filled cells without being stung by the bees. He told the children the bees could build a new layer of cells (called a honeycomb) in one night and begin right away to store pollen and honey in the new cells. He said a bee makes the honey by carrying the nectar in a honey sac where it is turned into honey inside the bee.

The Terry children saw worker bees fanning the waxy comb with their wings to cool it when the hive became too warm. They watched other bees guarding the entrance of the hive, touching antennae with the field bees when they came back with pollen and nectar and seeming to recognize them by doing this. They saw other worker bees cleaning the ground around the hives by removing dead bees or anything else they didn't want near their homes.

Most exciting of all was to watch the "observation hive" and see the dance of the returning bees after they had brought in a load of honey or nectar or pollen. It was hard to believe that other bees could tell from this dance what direction to take to find the very flowers from which the returning bee had come. But after the dance they saw other bees fly off in a "beeline," and Mr. Parker said they now knew just where to go!

It was a wonderful visit. After it was over the Terry children were glad whenever they heard the buzz and hum of bees in their garden. But there were other visitors that worried them, small crawling visitors that liked to eat the very vegetables the children enjoyed so much in salads and good buttery heaps on their plates at mealtime.

"I think it would be great if insects could read," said Tom. "I'd put up a sign: *Welcome if all you want is nectar and pollen.*"

INTRODUCTION TO THE EXPERIENCE TO FOLLOW

There is at the conclusion of this story a sentence or two that can make a study of caterpillars and butterflies follow naturally if the time of year and the weather are right for such an experience. Whenever the order followed in this volume is inappropriate for any reason there may be a backlog of promised experiences to turn to, arising from chance discoveries and interest expressed about some plant or creature during the study of one of the other subjects already explored.

If the group is to go on to caterpillars and butterflies the teacher may want a big garden picture which shows both bees and butterflies, or through conversation she may be able to explore enough possibilities that this subject will come from the children themselves. Children are easily attracted to the study of butterflies because of their beauty and variety.

Caterpillars and Butterflies

DEVELOPING THE EXPERIENCE

BY JUNE butterflies will have joined the flowers in gardens all over the country, but long before this the children may have made the acquaintance of caterpillars. This experience is apt to introduce itself even during the winter months. A child may discover the dangling hollow tube of a viceroy caterpillar hanging where it was made from a leaf of a tree. Or a black-and-red-brown woolly bear caterpillar may have crossed the road in front of a group out hiking in the fall. A moth pupa may have been found in the soil when the children were digging, for the large green sphinx moth caterpillar often tunnels several inches under the surface before entering the pupa stage.

It is good for leaders of a group of outdoor explorers to be prepared for an experience with caterpillars at almost any time of year. In preparation (and for inspiration) two books offer chapters that will fill almost any leader with eagerness for this experience. Donald Culross Peattie and his son Noel, authors of *A Cup of Sky,* in their chapters on pollen and on butterflies capture from their subject all the wonder which an adult must feel before the children he is leading can feel it. And Joseph Wood Krutch in *The Great Chain of Life* uses butterflies to take his readers close to some very large questions indeed as he discusses "The Need for Continuity."

For actual detailed information about caterpillars, butterflies, and moths there are excellent reference books for children
listed below. Their illustrations will teach as much as their text
to young children.

It is good to find these books urging that children collect
caterpillars rather than dead butterflies and moths. Raising
them to adulthood and watching the metamorphosis to its completion gives boys and girls a much more rewarding experience
than their parents had as youngsters with nets, cyanide bottles,
and mounting pins.

It is quite possible to begin the experience with the careful
caging of a female moth or butterfly, for in some varieties the
sexes can be distinguished by the wing patterns. Some females,
kept in a paper bag, will lay their eggs on the paper which can
be cut into pieces and pinned to the favorite leaves of the variety
needed, either right on the tree or in a net-covered jar. Then the
mother can be released. In books rcommended here, directions
are given for the care of several varieties during the egg-laying
period.

However, a vegetable garden can provide a more natural
observation. Cabbage butterflies are apt to be found hovering
over members of the cabbage-mustard family of plants, laying
eggs here and there. On some cabbage leaves the children may
be able to find tiny holes by using their magnifying glasses. If
one looks closely next to each hole there will be found a minute
newly hatched yellowish-green caterpillar. If the plant can be kept
fresh and growing under observation the children will be able to
watch the growth of these caterpillars and the moulting that oc-
curs as they grow until they reach the stage of changing into a
chrysalis. (The pupa of a butterfly is often called a chrysalis.)
Cabbage butterflies hatch from the egg in a week. Chrysalis cases
release the butterfly in ten days. The period of growth in between is rapid and interesting to watch. Thus three generations
of butterflies may be raised between one June and another, the
last one remaining inside the chrysalis through the winter.

Children raising a family of cabbage caterpillars can visit a
market and bring back leaves from many kinds of vegetables, discovering which ones belong to the cabbage-mustard family by

offering them to the caterpillars and seeing which are accepted as food. Certain weeds will qualify too. The hungry caterpillars can be fooled only if oil of mustard is spread on a leaf of some other kind of plant, or even on a piece of paper.

Black swallowtail butterflies (beautiful large green-and-black ones) as caterpillars like to feed on relatives of the carrot plant, including Queen Ann's lace. Monarch caterpillars prefer the milkweed plant, and are among the best varieties for observation by children because so much excellent supplementary material in pictures, stories, and films is available for classroom use featuring this amazing butterfly.

It is hoped that the children will learn about moths as well as butterflies, for these lovely night-feeding members of the order *Lepidoptera* are often of such spectacular size as to make them even more dramatic objects for observation than the more exquisite butterflies. Should the explorers come upon a tomato hornworm caterpillar (which also feeds on potato or tobacco plants as well as others of the same family) they will find it hard to keep up with the appetite of the growing creature until it is three or four weeks old, when it begins to shrink and darken. If dirt is placed in the jar or cage where it has been kept it will tunnel under. Here it will continue to wriggle and move about until it is a soft green pupa. If taken carefully from the soil after it stops wriggling, the pupa case will turn brown and hard while visible to the children. Now the "horn" of the caterpillar is gone, but there is a loop like the handle of a cup at one end. This protects the coiled tongue of the sphinx moth which will emerge. In a warm climate the pupa will open in a few weeks; in a cold climate it will remain in the ground until spring.

In Dorothy Sterling's book, *Caterpillars,* there are excellent directions given for caterpillar hunters in summer, fall, and winter. This book also describes and illustrates the amazing ways in which caterpillars are able to evade their many enemies.

In particular parts of the country certain kinds of butterflies and moths are doing special, typical things of such interest that children should be given a chance to see them if they are fortunate enough to be nearby. (If not they can read about many of them.) In scattered parts of California from as far north as Marin

County and south to San Diego, monarch butterflies make winter colonies. These fragile creatures migrate from Alaska and Canada to the farthest southern states and are believed to have crossed both oceans. In many parts of the South where colonies spend the winter local biologists should be able to tell exactly where they can be seen.

Whether or not children live in the Southwest they should hear about the yucca moth, and those who live near the desert where yucca plants grow should have the experience of observing the remarkable relationship between this moth and the plant. There is no more unlikely tale to be told of the interdependence of insects and flowers than this one. The leader may find it in *Cup of Sky* (mentioned above) and in Joseph Wood Krutch's *Voice of the Desert*. If a leader too far from the desert to arrange for direct observation is able to buy the dried pod of the yucca, often sold for winter bouquets, the children can see in each matured pod at least one hole made by the emerging yucca caterpillar when the plant was green and growing. This will make the story more real to the children. It is not unusual for insects to pollinate flowers, of course, but the way in which the yucca moth has been doing it for thousands of years is so dramatic in its difference that in resembles the work of college-taught plant breeders.

A hibernating butterfly that can be found even in cities in the winter time is the mourning cloak, which seeks a protected place — a crack or crevice inside a garage perhaps, or under a woodpile — and there spends the cold months apparently dead. If pinched gently, however, its legs will wiggle. This beautiful butterfly is even seen in city traffic during the summer, its black wings with a purplish sheen waving their borders of creamy yellow and flashing their rows of blue spots within the yellow band as they flutter through the air just above the cars and crowds on the street. After hibernating, when several warm days come in succession, the mourning cloak will come out to seek food and a mate, and the females will lay their eggs on willow, poplar, cottonwood, or elm trees.

During an experience with caterpillars, it is possible for

children to watch a life cycle, to observe instinctive behavior, to see dramatic examples of adaptation and (especially through the yucca moth) of interdependence. (There are few incidents recorded of learned behavior in insects, although a few observed cases are described in *Insects: Their Secret World* by Evelyn Cheesman, for many years curator of insects for the Zoological Society of London. Her book may be a resource if the children ever bring up the subject, "Can insects learn?" Any discussion of this kind is certain to leave the children with the very desirable understanding that much more remains to be learned about insects than is already known.)

At some time during the experience with caterpillars a film on the silkworm will add to the children's appreciation of their spinning abilities. Children know that moth caterpillars spin cocoons, but few know that some butterflies also do. They may have had the unpleasant experience of watching their fathers destroy tent caterpillars and have seen these silken tents, but not many are aware that all caterpillars spin, making a little path of silk wherever they go. If a young caterpillar didn't spin threads to cling to all over the leaf on which it hatches it might slip off, so it does this even before eating, instinctively. If one does fall it is held by a lifeline of silk and can ascend the thread. Children after seeing the silk-spinning process can hunt for spools of silk thread in their mother's sewing baskets and identify silk materials from cotton, wool, or synthetic weaves.

It will be good not to limit the hunting of caterpillars to gardens, for children should learn that in some cases these little creatures feed on weeds and other wild plants including trees and shrubs. They can be destructive in a garden, of course, but if it is a backyard garden, hand-picking is usually all that is needed to protect the plants, because toads, spiders, lizards, snakes, skunks, shrews, beetles, parasitic moths, and birds will all help with the destruction of the caterpillar surplus, *unless* all these natural enemies have been eliminated by the gardener! Even those in charge of commercial vegetable gardens are beginning to learn why biological rather than chemical deterrents are to the advantage of everyone.

OTHER POSSIBLE EXPERIENCES
WITH CATERPILLARS AND BUTTERFLIES

1. *The Butterflies Come,* listed among the books for children's use, is a story of the migration of the monarch butterfly, in this case those who winter in Monterey, California. This is an ideal storytelling book, easily adapted to both dramatization and dance, and one that holds great fascination for children.

2. If the leader will discover the varieties which are most common in the area it would be a good experience for the children to learn to identify some of the local butterflies. The leader can make large illustrations on poster board from a butterfly guide, and then each child could make his own booklet with the same pictures drawn by himself. If the opposite page is left blank it could be suggested that each child enter the date and place where he saw the butterfly, and if possible what flower, shrub, or tree it was on when he found it. This would be a limited experience, perhaps a half dozen butterflies, but a beginning for the child of careful observation and record keeping.

3. Little girls, and often the boys as well, may be interested in making large butterfly wings for themselves, each choosing a different butterfly (perhaps the ones to be identified). If these have a string at the neck, and strings to tie at the end of the arms, they will stay on. This might well suggest dancing to them, or it could be used in an identification game to help them in remembering the names before they go on their hunt together.

4. Inquiry among local biologists may turn up some people who are taking part in the study being made of monarch butterflies by banding them. A report from such a person would be fascinating, and he might be able to bring a butterfly with him and show the children how the banding is done. He could also report on what is learned by this process, again an introduction to children of the wider scope of adult interest in butterflies.

5. Butterflies are used even more widely than bees in decoration, and the children may spontaneously suggest adding to their "bee motif" collection another which uses butterflies and moths.

6. Butterflies are a particularly good subject for the writing of Japanese haiku, and the combination of butterflies and flowers would make the illustration of these haiku both colorful and interesting. The more children can learn to express their feelings, as one does in the writing of poetry, and not just "intellectualize" about these creatures they are studying, the deeper will be the learnings.

BOOKS FOR THE CHILDREN'S USE

Children's Books About Caterpillars, Moths, and Butterflies

Conklin, Gladys. *I Like Caterpillars*. Holiday.
Conklin, Gladys. *I Like Butterflies*. Holiday.
> Both of these books are particularly good for the younger children because they are selective and do not give too much information about too many varieties. Filled with suggestions and with excellent illustrations, they will do much to develop interest.

Goudey, Alice E. *Butterfly Time*. Scribners.
> A number of life cycles clearly described, as well as help in identification.

Hogner, Dorothy C. *Butterflies*. Crowell.
Hogner, Dorothy C. *Moths*. Crowell.
> Excellent books to have in the classroom, with a good deal of information presented in simple form.

Hussey, Lois J., and Pessino, Catherine. *Collecting Cocoons*. Crowell.
> Invaluable for the teacher and for the older children, this reference book gives many suggestions as to where one searches for cocoons, and what to do with them after they are found. Also useful in the identification of the cocoons which are found.

Marcher, Marion. *Monarch Butterfly*. Holiday.
> Particularly if the Politi book is used as an activity, this life cycle of the monarch should surely be used. It is excellent, and has suggestions for observing each life-cycle stage.

McClung, Robert M. *Tiger: The Story of a Swallowtail Butterfly*. Morrow.
> Another good life-cycle book, told in story form, and

emphasizing the hazards of the life cycle as well as its unfolding.

Politi, Leo. *The Butterflies Come*. Scribner.

A beautiful book, and one which arouses great interest among the children. See discussion under "Other Possible Experiences."

Smith, Arthur C. *Western Butterflies*. Lippincott.

Although regional, this has accurate pictures, fine life-cycle materials, and a number of instructions for hobbies which make it stimulating.

Sterling, Dorothy. *Caterpillars*. Doubleday.

Easily the best of the caterpillar books. Good drawings, attractive format, well written. Includes instructions for finding, feeding, and raising caterpillars.

Adult Books About Insects

Cheesman, Evelyn. *Insects: Their Secret World*. Morrow (Apollo Books).

Krutch, Joseph Wood. *The Great Chain of Life*. Houghton.

Krutch, Joseph Wood. *Voice of the Desert*. Sloane.

Peattie, Donald Culross, and Peattie, Neal. *A Cup of Sky*. Houghton.

These four books are all discussed and described in the section on "Developing the Experience." They will add much to the sensitivity of the leader's interpretation, as well as to his factual knowledge.

SONGS AND POEMS TO USE

"Queer Little Cradles": Number 25 in *We Sing of Life*.
"Fuzzy Wuzzy, Creepy Crawly": page 91 in *Poems To Grow On*.
"Caterpillar": Number 25 in *Martin and Judy Songs*.

STORY TO SUMMARIZE THE EXPERIENCE

FLYING FLOWERS

WHEN THE FIRST BUTTERFLIES APPEARED in the garden Alan and Ann wanted to catch them so they could see them better. There were many different kinds, most of them brightly colored, some large and some small, and they fluttered and flitted about so much like dancers that the children thought them as beautiful as the flowers.

"Like flowers that can fly," Ann told her mother as she tried to describe how she felt about them. "Can't I catch just one and keep it in a jar? Like the grasshoppers and the earthworms and spiders?"

"Butterflies are not so easy to keep in jars. They would try to get out, you know, and would beat their delicate wings against the glass. You wouldn't want them to injure their wings," her mother told her. "But you can find caterpillars and keep them until they change into butterflies. You have to learn what to feed them, of course."

"Will it be long before they turn into butterflies?" Ann asked sadly. She did so want a live butterfly to watch.

"Not very long at this time of year," said Mrs. Terry. "Let's look in a book and find out what kind changes quickly. It may be in our own garden."

The first caterpillar book Mrs. Terry found said that a cabbage caterpillar grows up quickly to be a butterfly, so Ann and Alan hurried to find Tom, who was in charge of the cabbage in the vegetable garden.

"Do you have any caterpillars in your cabbages?" she asked.

"I certainly do," grumbled Tom. "And I don't need them a bit. Why?"

"We need one," said Alan. "We're going to keep it for a pet until it turns into a butterfly."

Together the three children hunted among the cabbages. They found a plant with several small green shiny caterpillars chewing on its leaves and Tom picked them all off and dropped them into the jar. Alan carried the jar. Ann thought the little caterpillars very pretty. They were smooth and delicately colored, about the same shade of yellow-green as the cabbage leaves they had been eating.

"We need only one," said Alan. "What are you going to do with the others?"

"I'll put them under the cherry tree and let the robins find them. With all the birds around here, they'll never make it clear back to the cabbages. Birds need lots of food right now for their babies."

Ann took a piece of cabbage leaf, sprinkled a little water on it, and put it in the jar with the one caterpillar she and Alan chose. Soon it was busily eating the cabbage. Each day one of the children saw that their caterpillar had a fresh leaf. On the third day they were surprised to see that it wasn't eating. Instead it crawled to the top of the jar under the lid where many nail holes allowed air to come in. On the underside of the lid the caterpillar spun a little pad of silk to which its hind legs clung. While it was doing this, Alan put in a few twigs as the caterpillar book had suggested. Immediately the cabbage caterpillar spun a small loop attached to the nearest twig and stuck its head through the loop.

"Just like a safety belt," Alan said.

Now the caterpillar began to wriggle. Its green skin split and rolled back, as it had done several times before as the caterpillar grew too large for it, but this time there wasn't just another caterpillar underneath. There was a strange shape with no head or legs or eyes or mouth where the caterpillar had been before. The children knew this was a pupa, for they had been learning from their book. They knew it was often called a chrysalis, too, but Ann and Alan thought pupa was easier to say.

The pupa hung from its hind tip and its safety belt loop. It was a darker color than the caterpillar had been, just about the color of the underside of the jar lid from which it hung. It didn't look as though it was alive at all.

"Are you sure it isn't dead?" Ann asked often during the next ten days. Each day she and Alan marked the calendar so they would be sure to remember to watch on the tenth day when the pupa was supposed to open. When the day came the children carried the jar outside so it could be opened to allow the new butterfly to escape when it was ready.

Ann enjoyed fairy tales about enchantments and fairy princesses. She told her brother she was pretending a fairy story about the pupa.

"It's like a spell was holding our caterpillar in a little dark prison. Today the spell will be broken and instead of a caterpillar, a fairy will come out!"

Mrs. Terry heard this, and laughed as she saw Alan's wondering face.

Then she became serious. "It's really much more wonderful than your story, Ann. It isn't magic out of a fairy tale, either. This is something real and true. Inside the pupa case a wonderful change has been happening — but look!"

The pupa skin was cracking. Something was pushing out through the open place, something alive, crumpled, damp, and strange. It crawled to the stem of the nearest twig and rested a moment. The wrinkled wings began to dry and to unfold. Ann's "fairy" was a small butterfly with white upper wings with black tips. A few tiny black spots decorated these upper wings and the lower wings were a lemonish yellow, almost white. The little insect slowly waved its wings. Ann removed the lid of the jar. Her fingers trembled, she was so eager to see what would happen next. The wings, as lovely as the petals of a flower, looked as thin as tissue paper and she didn't want them to be injured. When the top was lifted, up and away the butterfly flew in a fluttering, dancing motion toward the bright-colored flowers in the garden.

Ann and Alan and Mrs. Terry ran to follow it, so all three saw the butterfly unroll her tongue and sip from the center of a nasturtium the drops of sweet nectar it needed for food. Soon it was impossible to tell which was Ann's and Alan's butterfly. Other cabbage butterflies were flitting about the garden, going from flower to flower.

"Will they carry pollen, too, like the bees?" asked Alan.

"Perhaps, although they have no pollen baskets on their legs," said Mrs. Terry. "But many insects that feed on nectar help to scatter the pollen from flower to flower, starting seeds growing for next year's garden."

Ann was dancing with excitement as she watched the butterflies.

"Alan, let's find some more caterpillars. We can find ever so many kinds if we look in all the places the book tells about. We can have a regular caterpillar zoo and feed each one what it needs. We can see moths come out, too. Some of them will stay in their pupas until spring and we can let them all out when it's warm again. Will you, Alan?"

When winter came, Alan and Ann had a collection of jars to watch over. Some held cocoons and some the chrysalis of a butterfly. Each jar had pasted on it the name of the caterpillar inside. There was also a little sponge to be moistened regularly so the inside of the jar wouldn't be too dry. Ann and Alan could hardly wait until spring to see the bright-colored "flying flowers" and the handsomely marked night-flying moths whose pictures they had seen in their caterpillar book.

Tom still argued with them about the caterpillars.

"O.K., perhaps the garden needs caterpillars, and caterpillars need the garden," he said, "but I'm glad there are so many birds and spiders and other creatures eating insects, or we wouldn't have any vegetables at all. I don't intend to raise cabbage butterflies; I want to raise cabbages!"

"Not me!" Ann replied. "I'd rather raise butterflies any time."

Alan settled the argument.

"Last year we had both. I think that's the best way."

INTRODUCTION TO THE EXPERIENCE TO FOLLOW

After talking about caterpillars in gardens, it is natural for the leader to suggest a search for other insects that eat green things. If it is grasshopper time, these large, active insects will make themselves known right away. Or the introduction can be made through talking about the color and motion butterflies add to our enjoyment of summertime, but without any *sound*. Are there any insects that provide music in the outdoors at this time of year? A listening-search can be made, as contrasted to a bird-watching trip. This time the children will use their ears, perhaps even closing their eyes part of the time to concentrate on listening. Bird song and other sounds will be recognized, and then, gradually the music of the insects which is so familiar that, like the ticking of a clock, it is often unnoticed.

EXPERIENCE WITH

Grasshoppers or Crickets

DEVELOPING THE EXPERIENCE

WHETHER GRASSHOPPERS OR CRICKETS are easier to find for this experience depends upon location and time of year. Children may become interested in both and proceed to learn about several varieties of similar insects although only one study was planned.

In preparation the leader must learn about the local varieties. There are two main divisions of the grasshopper family, the *shorthorns* or locusts which have short feelers and eat only vegetation, and the *longhorns* with long feelers. Some of the latter eat beetles, caterpillars, and other insects including dead of their own kind, in addition to seeds and greens.

There are also the crickets: tree crickets, mole crickets, and the common field cricket which likes barns and houses in winter. To complicate classification, some black grasshoppers of the longhorn variety are commonly called "Mormon crickets" and "sand crickets" but they have no wings and are not crickets at all!

In general the common varieties found in our country are located as follows:

Longhorn grasshoppers
    Katydids (large, green or pink). In northern and southern states, on twigs or leaves of plants.

"Mormon cricket" (large, black, wingless). In high mountains of the West.

" Sand crickets" (large head, wingless, black). On rocks and
sandy soil on the western coast.

Meadow grasshoppers (delicate, small to medium size). Common in wet fields and marshland.

Shorthorns, locusts

Red-legged grasshoppers (stout, strong-winged). All over the
United States in grass, except in western mountains.

Western or Rocky Mountain migratory locust (stout, strong
wings). In the Rocky Mountains and east to the Missis-
sippi Valley.

Clouded locusts (earthy brown, spotted, stout). In north-
eastern and southeastern states.

Carolina locusts (very large, brown or reddish or yellowish
with yellow edge on black hind wings). In North and
South Carolina and north to southern Canada. Common
along dusty roads.

Crickets

Mole cricket (big front feet for digging, black, wings flat on
back). Hard to find, living in burrows in the soil.

Snowy tree cricket (whitish, green, fragile with transparent
wings, good jumping legs). On West Coast and in the east
on shrubs and plants.

Common field cricket (black, stubby, wings flat on back). In
general over the country in hayfields, along roadsides, in
houses or barns, under porches, and so forth.

Often in early spring, children will discover what appears
to be a tiny grasshopper with a large head and no wings. This is
the nymph form of the young insect. It hatched when very small
from an egg laid on plant tissue or in the soil and in four or five
moults will be an adult with wings (if it is a winged variety).
There is no reason why the children should miss seeing this
growing process, for captive grasshoppers are easily fed and kept
healthy in a screened herbarium indoors or enclosed in a small-
mesh wire covering outdoors where weeds and grass are plentiful.

If the leader has learned a likely place for finding grasshoppers or crickets, there may be an outing planned in search of them, the cage prepared in advance. If the lively little musicians make themselves known before there is time for such preparation, each child can keep and care for one or two in a glass jar until the cage is ready.

Moulting is not the only interesting process to be observed. The children can discover that both grasshoppers and crickets are musicians. Students of the grasshopper have noted twelve different songs, each used for a different purpose by the insect. Usually only the males are singers. Some kinds of grasshoppers use their hind legs and fore wings to make their music; others have a file on the fore wing and a scraper on the back one and make their sounds by drawing the scraper over the file very rapidly. There is a crackling sound made when flying and a whirr when the wing cover rubs over the hind wings of the short-horn grasshoppers.

Although the children will not be able to see exactly how the music is made, they can observe that grasshoppers have two sets of wings when they are full grown. On the sides of their bodies are delicate "propellers" which fold in pleats like a fan. These are covered by tough upper wings which lift and carry the insect. In their observation cages the grasshoppers will demonstrate that they can hop slowly, climb, or just walk, although in the field they leap or fly in rapid zigzag difficult to follow.

As a rule grasshoppers live only from spring to early winter, but they may survive into a second spring. Far more nymphs are born than can survive the spring rains of a normal year. But there are occasional years when spring rains do not come to drown the usual number of newly hatched nymphs. These are the years of locust or cricket plagues. On pages 240 and 241 of M. R. Werner's *Brigham Young* is told the historic story of the terrible threat these plagues were to the Mormon settlers of Utah until they discovered that flocks of Franklin gulls would follow the hordes of insects and rescue the precious crops from destruction. These prairie gulls help to maintain the balance of life in the drier parts of the country. The leader of children interested in grasshoppers and crickets can tell them the simple dramatic story, showing pictures of the Franklin gull and of the monument in its honor in Salt Lake City. There is a book for older children which can be read aloud if the leader prefers, *The Coming of the Mormons* by Jim A. Kjelgaard, which tells about the settlers' battle with the insect hordes. Children may enjoy painting pictures of this drama, or acting it out. They are certain to remember it.

In contrast to their role as scourge and pestilence, grasshoppers (locusts) are still part of the diet of people in several parts of the world. Many stores carry canned grasshoppers among the more exotic imports and appetizers. While children are seldom interested in tasting strange foods, they will want to see the contents of the can if the leader can provide one, and a few of the more adventurous may try a taste.

Because crickets are used for fish bait and other commercial purposes, directions are easy to find for making cricket-breeding cages which can provide excellent cricket watching. State university agricultural extension services will not only send the instructions but often will stock the cage with male and female adult crickets in the proper number for it if this is desired.

Out-of-doors crickets pass the winter in the egg stage, or in warm climates may hatch into nymphs or grow to be adults and survive the winter. They are most plentiful in late summer.

Field crickets sing in chorus. They live during the day in burrows and come out at night. Certain localities will be favored every summer, year after year, while neighborhoods close by will have no crickets at all. No one has been able to explain why this is true.

Field crickets eat a number of other insects and a variety of plant and animal matter. Unfortunately they may acquire a taste for cloth and paper, and for this reason are not welcome in the house.

Tree crickets eat aphids and other small insects and some parts of trees or vines. They are usually soloists. Their song, a churry sound, is pitched differently from that of the field crickets. Only the male sings, or chirps, drawing one wing over the other. Teeth on the upper wing rub over a ridge on the lower.

Children fortunate enough to find the snowy tree cricket

in their neighborhood will be fascinated by its reputation for chirping faster on warm days, slowing down on cold days. A thermometer can be used to test this. The number of chirps per minute, divided by four and added to the number 40 should come out to be almost the exact temperature (Fahrenheit) registered on the thermometer.

In J. H. Fabre's classic *Social Life in the Insect World* the leader can read in advance about the life cycle of crickets to be seen in the breeding cage: courtship ritual, egg-laying in the sand, and three weeks later the emergence of the tiny nymphs which grow and moult until they are full-grown crickets.

One type of breeding cage is made from a 100-pound lard tin containing four inches of clean moist sand. A light bulb, suspended, will need to be large enough to keep the temperature at 80 to 90 degrees. Shredded paper piled in one section of the tin provides hiding places. A pan of poultry mash is placed on the sand. A waterer, supported so that it will keep a piece of cotton moist on an open dish, provides a safe drinking place in which young crickets cannot drown. A screen must be kept over the top of the lard tin and the top of its wall should be waxed so the insects can't crawl out when the cover is removed. In a cage of this size forty crickets, about half of them females, are recommended.

Individual crickets are used as pets in the Orient. In import shops one can find delicate bamboo cricket cages, but many of our American crickets are too small to be contained in them. Such a cage will add interest to a display to be acquired for the classroom as this experience goes on. Factual books, poetry, stories, pictures, and toys inspired by crickets and grasshoppers will add to the children's pleasure as they watch and listen to their living insect musicians indoors and out.

OTHER POSSIBLE EXPERIENCES WITH
CRICKETS AND GRASSHOPPERS

1. Observation of crickets with special attention to their various ways of jumping, walking, hopping, and flying should lead into experimentation on the part of the children with the duplica-

tion of as many of these movements as they can achieve. This would be a natural rhythmic activity which could easily become a grasshopper or cricket dance. It could be done in connection with the second activity suggested below.

2. Listening to cricket and grasshopper "songs" in the field or from a recording of insect sounds could lead into the making of music with a whirring device, some paddles that have been roughened (perhaps with sandpaper) and can be rubbed together, and practice in making the chirping sounds orally. These primitive musical effects could then be put together into a "cricket chorus" to accompany the dance worked out above.

3. Introducing, or reintroducing, the Japanese haiku by the use of Harry Behn's *Cricket Songs* (a collection of haiku published by Harcourt Brace) could lead to interesting writing of this verse form. If haiku have been used extensively during the year the children may want to branch out into other forms of poetry writing. Any collection of haiku will contain some poems that are about the cricket.

4. This is a unit which lends itself to the use of literary material with which the children can extend their newly found information into the field of fantasy, both deepening their interest in these insects and helping them to distinguish between fantasy and fact (as well as the pleasure of the stories themselves). George Selden's *Cricket in Times Square* (Farrar, Straus and Cudahy) for the older children; Walt Disney's *Pinocchio* with the co-hero called Jiminy Cricket; or the Aesop fable about the "Ant and the Grasshopper" would be examples of these. There are others which any librarian will help the leader find.

BOOKS FOR THE CHILDREN'S USE

> Bronson, Wilfred S. *The Grasshopper Book*. Harcourt.
>> This is an excellent and accurate book, older than the Hogner book but just as useful.
>
> Caudill, Rebecca. *A Pocketful of Cricket*. Holt.
>> Although a story rather than a factual book, this is not fantasy in the sense of *The Cricket in Times Square,* and will be useful with the younger children.

Hogner, Dorothy Childs. *Grasshoppers and Crickets.* Crowell.
Helpful information, with strong clear pictures. More attractive than Bronson, although both are good and sound.

Selden, George. *The Cricket in Times Square.* Ariel (Farrar, Straus and Cudahy).
This is very well done fantasy, and should delight the children as well as being the kind of book which might well lead to dramatization.

SONGS AND POEMS TO USE

"The Cricket": page 90 in *Poems To Grow On*.

STORY TO SUMMARIZE THE EXPERIENCE

CHILDREN NEED GRASSHOPPERS

IN THE SAME BLOCK as the Terrys' house was a vacant lot where there was no building, only grass. The grass grew all summer without being cut, and this was the place where the children loved to hunt grasshoppers. They called it "Grasshopper Land" because so many grasshoppers lived there.

Ann, Alan, and Tom and their friends took glass jars into the vacant lot and ran about hunting grasshoppers in the tall green jungle. They didn't catch many because it wasn't easy.

The littlest grasshoppers were the easiest to catch because they hadn't grown wings yet and couldn't fly. They could jump in all directions with their strong back legs, and they did. Just as Ann would be ready to pop her glass jar over a small green grasshopper, off it would jump, zigzagging as it went, and she had no way of knowing which direction its next great leap would take. It might land right on her head and then jump clear over a tall weed several feet away.

The children shouted with laughter while they ran here and there trying to catch a grasshopper to put in the jars.

"Why do you catch them?" Ann's mother asked.

"Oh, I don't know. Children need grasshoppers, I guess," Ann explained.

Mrs. Terry thought a moment and remembered that she had caught grasshoppers, too, when she was a little girl.

One day Ann was quick and careful and lucky. She caught two large grasshoppers in one hour. She put plenty of green grass in the jar, and of course there were holes in its lid so air could get inside. She took her captives home and sat down on the edge of the sandbox under the cherry tree where it was shady and cool. She watched the two grasshoppers climbing slowly and carefully up a long blade by holding it steady with their front feet while they chewed along the edge of the grass with busy little jaws.

Ann noticed what large eyes the grasshoppers had. No wonder they had been hard to catch. They should be able to see things moving very far away with their large eyes.

As she watched them, Ann discovered that her two grasshoppers were different. One of them had a rounded end in the back, while the other was pointed. She wondered why they weren't alike.

Whenever the Terry children wanted to find out something they looked for a book with pictures. Ann told Tom, who was allowed to go to the library alone, that she would give him one of her grasshoppers if he would get a book about them with good pictures so she could find out why they were not alike.

"O.K.," said Tom. "I'll go right now."

When he came back from the library Tom was grinning. He had found a fine grasshopper book. It had pictures just like both of the insects in Ann's jar.

"Guess what!" he said. "The one with the pointed end is the female and she sticks that point into the ground when she lays her eggs. It's called an egg placer."

"Why does she want the eggs to be down in the ground?" asked Ann. "I should think she would put them in a little nest somewhere."

"Well, it says here that she squirts foamy glue all around them and covers them with bubbles, and then the glue hardens and protects the eggs until the babies are ready to hatch out in the spring."

"That's pretty much like a nest," said Ann. "Look. She's

cleaning her eyes and her little feelers. She's using her feet to do it."

Tom said he would take the male grasshopper, and off he went for a jar to put it in.

Both of Ann's grasshoppers had wings because they were full grown. There were two sets of wings. One pair folded up under the others. The top one lifted and carried the grasshoppers, and the folded ones opened out to act like propellers. When the grasshoppers were flying the children said they sounded as if they had motors. They made a whirring noise like a tiny airplane.

Ann was glad she could keep the mother grasshopper. She wanted to see it lay eggs.

Tom was glad she had given him the father grasshopper because he had been reading in the library book and had found something Ann didn't know. The father grasshoppers usually make the music. They have rows of tiny points on the thickest part of their hind legs close to their bodies. They rub these points across the hard ridge on their wings and make a singing noise. Tom hoped his grasshopper would do this if he kept it happy by giving it plenty to eat and drops of water to drink.

Ann put some dirt in the bottom of her jar, but she didn't see the mother grasshopper place any eggs in it. She watched it often for three days.

Tom put his jar in the bedroom, but he didn't hear his grasshopper make any music. He listened often for three days.

On the fourth day both children began to worry about their captives.

"Let's take them back to Grasshopper Land," suggested Ann. "Mine doesn't look happy in this jar."

"I know," said Tom. "They can't fly around. O.K., let's take them back."

When the children carried their glass jars to Grasshopper Land they saw a robin fly up from the grass with a grasshopper in his beak. They met Mrs. Cat coming from the vacant lot. They knew she liked to go hunting there, too, although she wasn't as good at catching grasshoppers as the birds were.

"Maybe we shouldn't let them go. They may get eaten," said Ann.

"I know," said Tom, "but you want yours to lay eggs in the ground so there'll be new babies in the spring. And mine won't make any music in this jar. I think he wants to be free to jump and fly around."

"Yes," Ann agreed. "If a bird eats them, that's all right, I guess. They would probably die in the cold winter anyway and the birds need them for food. But we don't need them in these jars any more."

They told their friends what they were doing. All the children who had grasshoppers in jars decided to let theirs go too. They hoped the cold winter wouldn't kill all the singing, hopping grasshoppers. They wanted to have fun next summer running through Grasshopper Land trying to catch new families to watch for a while.

It was fun to turn the captives free and watch them escape, whirring into the tall grass. Tom heard one singing. He thought it was probably his.

Alan didn't catch any grasshoppers that summer, but he listened one night to all the sounds coming from his backyard after he was in bed.

"I'll never know what makes them all," he thought. "It takes so many live things to keep a backyard going. But tomorrow I'll hunt for the cricket under the back steps. I wonder what he needs and what needs him. I wonder . . ." But the soft, drowsy backyard music had put him to sleep before he finished wondering.

INTRODUCTION TO THE EXPERIENCE TO FOLLOW

Since the next session will be a review no special introduction is needed. The leader may suggest to the children that they try to think about all the experiences they have had together. The leader will also want to put the books which have been most enjoyed during the course onto the browsing table, and to put up many pictures which will remind the group of their recent experiences.

Remembering Together

SUMMARIZING THE COURSE

WHENEVER a group of children who have shared experiences are about to end their time together and scatter for vacation activities or to enter new groups, the leader longs to discover if possible what has been happening to them as a result of their time together. Have they formed any new concepts? Do they look at their world differently now? Has the series of explorations added any new ideas to the ever-growing personal religion of each child, of which he may be quite unconscious?

Kindergarten and primary children will find it impossible to verbalize what the leader is so eager to know. Following such experiences as this book outlines they may be able to draw pictures of a "backyard" including everything they think it needs. As a joint project they might make a model of one in a sand table. During the process of these activities the children will talk, and what they say may help the leader estimate what they have learned from their experiences.

Older children may be able to choose "parts" from the list of characters in the experiences: one becoming a robin, one a cat, one a cricket, and so on. Then each character can tell the others what it needs from them, and what it will do for them.

The robin might tell the earthworm, "I will eat some of you. You will starve if there are too many earthworms."

Then he could address the cherry tree. "I will help plant your seeds by dropping them far from your branches."

The children's pleasure in doing this will come from being allowed to act as authors of their own lines. If more than one desires the same role there can be several grasshoppers, for instance, each making a different observation. Knowing the children well by this time, the leader should be able to plan this game to suit them and their abilities. If it could be recorded on a tape recorder the result might be well worth keeping. Children are fascinated to hear their own "play" played back to them, and it would be useful for playing to the parents at some time to show some of the children's learnings.

Acting out the interdependence of all that lives in the backyard may be too complicated for some groups. The creative act can be one of jointly composing a poem or story. The leader, chalk in hand, could ask, "Who will be the robin and tell what he will do for the cherry tree?" "Who will be the cherry tree and tell what it will do for the robin?" Each reply can be written on the blackboard or recorded on a tape (or one could do both at the same time). The result might be similar to this, for example:

The robin said to the cherry tree: *I will plant your seeds.*
The cherry tree told the robin: *Build your nest here and
    eat my cherries.*
*Soil, I am making you richer and giving you air pockets
    for roots* is what the earthworm said.
*Earthworm, find your food in me and use me for your
    home* said the soil.

It is obvious that this would become tedious if carried out to anything like completion of all the relationships, but a little of it would serve to show both leader and chidren how much they know about the "characters" in the backyard drama of life. It would also show how their living is like a web of interwoven strands of giving and taking, even though they are not aware of it. This will summarize the principal meaning of the previous experiences for the children.

Children enjoy a survey hour in which the leader reminds

them of what they have done through a "Do You Remember?"
game. Each can draw from a basket the reminder of a single experience. ("We hunted for nests," for example.) Each would
then be allowed a little time in which to recall and think about
that experience. (In case a child draws the reminder of an experience he missed he can trade with another child.) Then each,
in turn, would tell briefly what happened that day and what he
learned from it.

There is, of course, no way in which teachers, leaders, or
parents can discover the total impression any series of experiences has had on any given child or group of children. If the
adult has learned, the children have learned even more. In fact,
such a "Do You Remember?" game is not complete unless the
leader draws a reminder, too, and takes a turn at remembering
aloud.

Long years from now teachers, leaders, and parents will
have their answer if they are fortunate enough to find any grown
members of this exploring group continuing their exploration of
the natural world with lively interest and intelligent reverence
for life in all its forms. Or perhaps he might find one of the now-
grown class members working in the field of conservation,
whether as an individual or professionally. Basic attitudes which
are really fostered endure longer than many of us realize.

Albert Schweitzer has written,

> As we know life in ourselves, we want to understand life
> in the universe, in order to enter into harmony with it.
> Physically we are always trying to do this. But that is not
> the primary matter; for the great issue is that we shall
> achieve a spiritual harmony. Just to recognize this fact is
> to have begun to see a part of life clearly.[1]

The spirit of any child benefits from discovering a natural
harmony where he once saw only misunderstood savagery. The
more he learns from studying life around him, the nearer he
comes to that feeling of security in his universe that is described
by Thor Heyerdahl in *Kon Tiki:*

[1] Charles R. Joy, *Albert Schweitzer: An Anthology* (Harper and Brothers),
page 219.

The closer we came into contact with the sea and what had its home there, the less strange it became and the more at home we ourselves felt.[2]

A poet might call this "feeling more at home," a growing awareness of the pervading, universal Great Spirit of some American Indians, called by many names and imagined in many forms by the people of the earth, and symbolized in our language by the word *God*. If our children seek to understand life in all its forms, the source of life and the source of love (which seems to accompany the passing on of life in its higher forms), their quest for the truth about the ultimate mysteries may be even more rewarding than our own.

[2] Thor Heyerdahl, *Kon Tiki* (Rand McNally), page 159.

APPENDIX

AT LEAST in the northern and middle states across the country, the following sequence would work out best. The southern states and the milder Pacific coastal regions could adopt different order, and sometimes substitutions may have to be made for specific plant or animal life.

September: getting acquainted through the work party, digging for kinds of soil, and discovering earthworms. Begin study of earthworms.

October: complete earthworm study, and begin experiences with robins, including finding old nest and trying to make one. Last session of the month introduce the cat study through Halloween myths.

November: study cat adaptations and greater cat family, leading to tree study. Choose tree to adopt and visit with tree expert. Begin woodpecker study.

December: build feeder and box houses for flickers. Make suet decorations for trimming a Christmas tree for the winter birds.

January: begin study of spiders (introduced at the end of the tree study). This will take several sessions and lead to other insect eaters, the mole and shrew families.

February: continue the mole and shrew experiences, leading into the study of ants, who also as a rule live in the ground. Make an ant house which can, when the class is through with it, be given to a suitable school for handicapped children, or find a similar use for it. This leads into the experience with grass.

March: the contribution grass makes leads naturally into the plants of the garden, and will make possible the inclusion of flowers and vegetables. This ties in with the flowers always used at the Easter season.

April: if Easter is late butterflies may be used for a study for that special day, leading into the experience with bees.

May: bees will be the subject for at least half of May, and then lead into the grasshopper and cricket experience.

June: grasshopper and/or cricket experience introduces music which may lead to the final experience in which the children will retrace the interwoven nature of life in their "remembering experience."

It is not important that the order of this suggested approach be used, for no matter where one begins in the web of life it is possible to trace the interrelatedness and the interrelationships. The leader who is familiar with all the material in this book will be alert to watch for the spontaneous expressions of interest on the part of the boys and girls and capitalize on these in planning the order of events for this exploration of the living environment.

DESERT ADAPTATION OF THE MATERIALS *by* MARGARET GOODING

Experience with sand: this is surely most applicable.

Experience with earthworms: applicable in irrigated areas. Sow bugs are also prevalent and could be substituted.

Experience with robins: The cactus wren is best for study in this region, or others of our desert birds.

Experience with the cat: no problems.

Experience with trees: in irrigated areas citrus and date palms are advised for study. In pure desert areas the palo verde and mesquite will offer interesting contrast, especially in their particular leaf structure which conserves liquid. The role spacing plays in desert ecology should be emphasized here.

Experience with spiders: applicable for sure! Because of the prevalence of the black widow in desert areas extra care should be taken on web-collecting expeditions.

Experience with the woodpecker: the relationship of the woodpecker to the cactus and other desert plants should be studied.

Experience with ants: we have many of them.

Experience with grass: applicable in irrigated areas. Study of the desert after rain will yield interesting grass-like plants and lead to the question of what do all those cattle on the desert ranges eat.

Experience with a garden: applicable in irrigated areas, but should be done in February. This experience could be enlarged upon if an irrigated and an unirrigated garden could be set up side by side.

Experience with bees: no problem and special kinds of desert honey can be studied.

Experience with moles and shrews: these seem to be more of a problem, but it would seem that mice could be substituted where these are not easily found.

Experience with grasshoppers or crickets: these are available for study, but special local varieties should be considered.